Science and Society: A Symposium

Science and Society: A Symposium

Contributors

Adlai E. Stevenson
Bertram D. Thomas
R. L. Sproull
John Bardeen
Jerome B. Wiesner
William O. Baker

XEROX

Xerox Corporation
Rochester, 1965

Science and Society: A Symposium

Copyright © 1965 by Xerox Corporation, Rochester, New York
All rights reserved. Manufactured in the United States of America
Published by W. A. Benjamin, Inc., New York, New York 10016
Library of Congress Catalog Card Number: 65-28045

Foreword

This volume consists of papers delivered by a group of distinguished Americans who honored us by participating in our dedication of a new laboratory for basic research at Xerox Corporation in Webster, New York, on November 12, 1964. All the papers but one are the work of men who are leaders in important areas of scientific endeavor, a capacity in which they have had to relate their contributions to the broader problems of society. The remaining contributor is the late Ambassador Adlai Stevenson, who addresses himself here to the significance of science in international policies and problems.

The authors largely address themselves to the impact of science on society, but in some papers one can also note discussion of the reverse influence. We have chosen the title *Science and Society: A Symposium* to suggest the presence of both of these interactions. At the same time, by including the second part of the title, we intend to imply that these are individual commentaries, quite worthy but in no sense constituting a definitive treatment of such an immense subject. We have arranged the sequence in a manner offering some continuity between successive papers.

In our rapidly changing world, it may be appropriate to remind the reader that these remarks were presented in November 1964. We regard them as still timely and worthy of publication. With the concurrence of the authors, the remarks have been edited somewhat for purposes of written presentation.

We are indebted to Winfield W. Tyler, Head of the Research Division, Xerox Corporation, for his role in organizing the Symposium; to Harold E. Clark, Scientific Director, Research Division, for assistance in preparing this volume; and to William A. Benjamin, our publisher, and his staff, particularly Mrs. Lenore R. Stevens, for guidance and editorial help.

John H. Dessauer

Executive Vice-President
Research and Engineering Divisions

Rochester, New York
September 1965

Contents

Science and Society: A Symposium

Science and Technology
in the Political Arena

The late Adlai E. Stevenson
United States Representative to the United Nations

I am wondering how I ever had the temerity to accept this invitation to participate in a discussion on science and technology. Here I am surrounded by distinguished scientists — and I know nothing about science; surrounded by great industrialists and businessmen — and I've been in foreign affairs so long I've all but forgotten what makes the world's wheels turn; surrounded by intellectuals — and my only claim to membership in that group rests on the columnists' conclusion that if one's sentences are moderately grammatical he must be an "intellectual."

I suppose the only explanation is bravado — or perhaps a hope that someone might think I really belong in company such as this.

I am reminded of the callow new member of the House of Commons who asked Disraeli if he should participate actively in the debates. And, after a quick appraisal the Prime Minister replied: "No, I think not; it would be better for people to wonder why you didn't speak rather than why you did."

But I take some comfort from the thought that being a diplomat may excuse me from being an authority on science and technology. Moreover, I have no worry that my colleagues and I will be replaced by automation.

I also have found some satisfaction in rereading only recently some predictions for the future published in 1937. President Roosevelt asked a committee of leading scientists and engineers to prepare a forecast of probable inventions and technological developments over the next quarter century.

At the time it seemed to present dazzling and daring prospects. But reading it again today, one is struck far less by what it did predict than by what it didn't. And I find myself on a par with the greatest scientific minds of the time — for I, too, failed to foresee nuclear energy, antibiotics, radar, the electronic computer, and rocketry.

YESTERDAY . . . TODAY . . . TOMORROW

But I suppose I must begin my task — to relate the world of my endeavors to that of yours. In so doing, I am reminded of what a French philosopher said at the end of the last century: "Science has promised us truth — an understanding of such relationships as our minds can grasp; it has never promised us either peace or happiness."

Yesterday, most of mankind could look forward only to a life that would be "nasty, brutish and short," on the verge of privation in good years, starving when the harvests failed. Now wheat pours out of our ears. We swim in milk. We are threatened with vegetable and fruit surpluses and even, in some happy years, wine gluts as well. Water, man's precious resource, will be captured from the oceans by desalinization; nuclear power promises unlimited energy; the rocket, unlimited speed; electronics, unlimited technical control. All the old locks of scarcity have been sprung, the prisons flung open. From the first stone tool to the cell which snaps a camera shutter on the far side of the moon, the stride of man's abundance is all but unimaginable — and yet it is here.

And what can still be foreseen by scientists humbles me. For example, in the field of communications (to which this new Research and Engineering Center of Xerox is dedicated), live television may soon be commonplace all over the world. We may use satellites for transmission of the mail. David Sarnoff goes further: In our grandchildren's world, he assures us, it will be possible to communicate with anyone anywhere, at any time, by voice, sight, or written message — separately or as a combination of all three. Ultrahigh and microwave radio frequencies and laser beams can provide billions of channels, so that each person in the world can have his own, much as he can now have his own telephone number.

The international implications of such instant transmittal of information are staggering — and the possibilities for wrong numbers are even more staggering!

THE BASIC MIRACLE OF MODERN TECHNOLOGY

Against this background of vast wealth and steady growth, let us throw off some of the anxieties which have shadowed our thinking about the vast opportunities and responsibilities this wealth creates. There is less talk these days — even during that strange interlude we call a presidential campaign — about "spending ourselves into bankruptcy," or "inflation hurrying us to ruin," or "the menace of growing Federal Debt" — which, incidentally, has actually fallen in proportion to national income.

But we still talk of the difficult choices between public and private expenditure. We still hear the question raised of this or that program — for housing, urban renewal, education — whether we can afford it or whether it may not "overstrain" our capacity.

These questions, I believe, are valid in the short run — while we train new skills (or install new computers) and build new plants. But the science and technology which we acclaim today is making these questions irrelevant in the longer run because our economy can grow to meet each new charge made upon it. It will stagnate only if we do not ask enough.

This is the basic miracle of modern technology. This is why it is, in a real sense, a magic wand which gives us what we desire. Don't let us miss the miracle by underestimating this fabulous new tool. We can have what we want. This is the astonishing fact of the modern scientific and technological economy. This is the triumph we hail today. This is the new instrument of human betterment that is at our hand if we are ready to take it up.

EFFECTIVE UTILIZATION OF THE NEW TECHNOLOGY

If we are to do so effectively, however, I suggest two things are necessary. The first is to recognize that in our modern highly productive market economy, stability and growth depend upon partnership between management, labor, and government.

Today, our sophisticated fiscal management allows government to gear its expenditures and its taxation to the general movements of the economy and to increase the smoothness and reliability of expansion. A practical public-private partnership is a necessity and has become a fact.

Or take the question of a short-term overloading of demand — in other words, inflation. Throughout the Atlantic World, leaders in the modern market economies recognize that the biggest inflationary pressure — not the only pressure, but the biggest — comes from the wage-cost push: wages rising more rapidly than productivity and pushing too much demand into the economy for existing supply. There is no way of countering this risk save a genuine understanding and partnership between government, setting the overall guide lines, and management and labor, cooperating with noninflationary wage settlements.

The first principle of the new abundance is, thus, partnership in the mixed economy.

The second is an end to the quarrel between public and private purposes. In an economy growing by thirty billion dollars a year, it is nonsense to say that expanded education, decent housing, an end to urban ghettos, recreation, antipollution measures — to name only the top human priorities on the public list — can be secured only by the sacrifice of private opportunity.

If, through effective partnership, we keep the present steady rates of growth, we can add some six billion dollars in public money at the federal level without adding a single tax. Such sums, distributed in part to states and cities, could give a wholly new impetus to better living and to the end of grinding poverty for the minority among us who still don't share our incredible prosperity. This is a by-product of extraordinary growth.

I would go further and say that unless public and private needs are satisfied together, the private sector will begin to suffer the consequences. Our public decisions will shape our private decisions. Don't let us make unreal distinctions. Let us see these public and private needs as interdependent. For the citizen is an amphibian — private in his loves and purposes, public in his needs and responsibilities. The glory of modern science is that it allows him to act freely in both spheres. Let him recognize this new freedom and accept this new enfranchisement. If he does, I don't doubt that we can build a human city worthy of our tools, as soaring as our science, as useful as our technology, and restored to its true purpose: the well-being of man.

THE WORLDWIDE RESPONSIBILITIES OF SCIENCE

But, as the French philosopher said a long time ago, science has never promised us either peace or happiness. And if it does now, it can never be exclusive; it can never be just American peace and happiness. Because science has also shriveled our world and packed the human family into an even smaller house.

We are told that a host of techniques to ease man's burdens cannot be used because we do not know how to bring adequate resources — money, labor, and materials, and most of all, management — to bear on the problems. But I submit that here, too, successful efforts are being made all over the world to apply what we know in order to correct what exists.

An example is the transfer of science and technology from one country to another. In this company, Xerox, I believe there has been such transfer of communications know-how to its Japanese counterpart, Fuji Xerox. The problem becomes more difficult in countries whose scientific development and markets are less developed. We know, for example, that China can develop an atom bomb by concentrating a large fraction of its scientific effort and industrial resources. But the cost in living standards is high.

You will forgive me if I emphasize particularly the activity of the United Nations in the application of science and technology. This is a political effort in the world community as it was in our own community.

Electricity had been harnessed fifty years in the United States before it was put to work on the farm. It was political will that put it there.

It was political initiative which built TVA, the Grand Coulee Dam, the super highways, years after we knew how.

It was a political trigger which started the huge programs of research in science in universities and private industry.

And it is also political will which has inspired the members of the United Nations to establish programs of technical assistance. For we know that peace can never be secure when half the world envies the other half.

The United States and the very few countries which can produce more than they consume cannot be the stackers of wheat and the hog butchers for the whole world. To keep the peace, therefore, the United Nations is very much concerned with what science can do to produce more of everything.

Winston Churchill said: "It is quite certain that mankind would not agree to starve equally, and there might be some very sharp disagreements about how the last crust of bread was to be shared."

Since the depression we have gradually rid ourselves of the Robin Hood notion that to give to the poor we must rob the rich. We discovered nationally that everyone is better off in an affluent society. And although we have not yet won our own war on poverty, we have long abandoned the concept that it must be shared to be reduced.

The United Nations rejects that concept, too.

Let me give you some examples of projects in almost a hundred countries in which the United Nations Special Fund is helping developing countries to help themselves.

In water resources, there are ninety-one projects under way. One is the Mekong Delta in Southeast Asia, where the river basin could be used for irrigation, flood control, and electric power — if it wasn't used for war!

Others include desalinization, which could have been available commercially by the early 1950's — if we had spent one-tenth of what the Manhattan Project cost us to develop the atomic bomb!

In fisheries there are twenty-two projects to increase the harvest from the seas.

In locust control, projects in thirty-eight countries may soon bring this ancient scourge under control.

And just a week before the dedication of this Xerox center, agreement was reached to eradicate the rhinoceros beetle, which causes severe damage to the coconut palm in the South Pacific, including islands under United States administration. All kinds of methods will be tried — insecticides, cultivation of deadly parasites, sterilization of the male through radiation — a peaceful use of atomic energy — except to a rhinoceros beetle!

One hundred countries are cooperating in a world weather watch. In two years our satellites have discovered twenty hurricanes, typhoons, and other storms and observed the behavior of sixty-two others. Nothing, of course, is more global than the weather and the world is getting together to do something about it at last — Mark Twain to the contrary notwithstanding.

1965: INTERNATIONAL COOPERATION YEAR

As you may know, 1965 has officially been designated International Cooperation Year. Many people ask, why a special year? Isn't the United Nations itself founded "to save succeeding generations from the scourge of war," the essence of cooperation on a full-time basis?

Of course, international cooperation should not and does not have a starting date or a finishing date. The special year was originally suggested by Prime Minister Nehru to give a "truer picture" of the United Nations to the world, by calling attention to its cooperating elements — not its conflicts.

Incidentally, an elderly lady in Seattle had an idea along these lines. "Why couldn't the delegates," she wrote me, "take a break every twenty minutes or so, and go out into the corridors and sing songs? Surely this would show the delegates that they could be in harmony at some point."

While I welcome all suggestions for reducing friction among nations, I felt obliged to point out the practical difficulties to her proposal. I'm afraid group singing would only increase the discords.

Our television viewers have some very good advice, too. A school teacher wrote that she admired me very much, but there was one thing I should know. "Your posture at the Security Council is *negative*. Please sit up straight so you'll make a good impression on the underdeveloped nations."

Much as I like TV — and I have even come to accept the accuracy of its picture of me — neither the camera nor the press has given a full picture of the United Nations. But I am sure the Xerox programs will help to fill it out.

Most public interest in the United Nations centers on its peacekeeping activity, on the polemics of the cold war, on conflict, not cooperation. Yet, in fact, only 2500 of the 23,000 members of the staff of the United Nations and its specialized agencies are working on peace-keeping operations; the other 20,000 are working on peace-building operations.

Nonetheless, the enormous contribution the UN is making toward economic progress — helping countries to leap into the twentieth century — is scarcely comprehended, even by the well-informed. A newspaperman explained the lack of publicity this way: "If you build a 57-story building in the heart of Manhattan, you'll get a mention in the Real Estate Section. But if you blow up a 2-story building anywhere, you'll make the front page."

Reading so much about disagreements, some people get the idea that they are total. But it is nonsense to assume that if two countries oppose each other on topic A, they also necessarily oppose each other on B through Z.

I need not list for you the topics upon which we are in disagreement with the Soviet Union. You know them. But do you know that we cooperate with the Soviet Union in allocating radio frequencies, forecasting the weather, managing air transport, fighting disease, studying the oceans?

Many of these projects involve multilateral cooperation. For example, since 1962, some forty-four vessels from twenty nations have been making an intensive study of the Indian Ocean's twenty-eight million square miles — 14 per cent of the earth's surface — which is relatively unexplored.

The projects, large and small, are fascinating. But the point is that International Cooperation Year is nothing new. It is simply unfurling a banner over what has been going on for more than fifteen years.

When ICY was designated by the General Assembly, our Delegate said:

We are engaged in nothing less than a massive and historically unique effort to transfer and adapt science and technology from the limited areas in which they have flourished to the international com-

munity as a whole . . . . If more people can begin to grasp the fact of this great development — if they can begin to sense its significance — if they can share some of the hope that it justifies, they will appreciate better the pioneering work of the UN in its adolescent years.

While many instances of international cooperation are not under the direct auspices of the UN — such as the Indian Ocean project — they have all been inspired by UN philosophy and strengthened by its encouragement.

THE GENEVA MEETING OF WORLD SCIENTISTS

When the United Nations Conference on the Application of Science and Technology to the Developing Areas met in Geneva, it focused the attention of the world's scientists for the first time directly upon the world's needs. It gave all the countries represented the opportunity to find out what others were doing. It was an attempt to put all the activities of all the countries into proper perspective and to determine priorities. It was a tremendous pooling of knowledge. The American contribution of printed material alone was twelve volumes, compiled by our industrial and scientific community.

That conference was a turning point in human history — the first collective international attempt to marshal and apply the world's resources in science and technology to man's needs.

CURRENT CRISES

I have discussed hurriedly the achievements and prospects for scientific cooperation. They are heartening, but we have barely touched upon the most urgent items on the agenda.

Education at Every Level. Half the world cannot read, and at our present rate of teaching it will take fifty years before the developing countries have the specialists they need.

Population Control. In hundreds of thousands of years, the world's population reached a billion and a half, but in the past sixty years it reached three billion.

It is a phenomenon of the twentieth century that the crisis and the means to meet it arrived simultaneously. The question for the future is whether we can apply the means — in time.

ROLE OF GOVERNMENT

The role of government is to create a favorable climate and a steady stimulus for every force that can benefit mankind.

America has been operating on this principle. The American experiment is essentially a great partnership, which our Government has both encouraged and participated in. Universities, private enterprise, charitable foundations, and government agencies have all contributed to our scientific progress and prosperity.

In the United States, our once heterogeneous collection of states might be compared to the diversity among the nations today. And as our Federal Government has provided the central impetus to reduce the differences in standards of living among our states, so indeed can the United Nations assume much the same role in the world.

Last week I was in Latin America, and I was struck again by the paradox of her past and her present. This great continent was settled hundreds of years ago. Yet the scientific developments of later years have not been explored there because Latin America is still trying to find its way politically. The major function of the Alliance for Progress is to provide the impetus and to help roll away the ancient obstacles.

So it is by political action and political determination — nationally, regionally, and internationally — that we shall put to work effectively the great fund of knowledge already in the public domain and that is still to come from great research centers like the one here at Xerox.

That is one of the great missions of the UN — to help clear the way politically for the advancement of science and technology, and the limitless blessings they can bring to mankind.

Our New Civilization: An Age of Research

Bertram D. Thomas
President, Battelle Memorial Institute

The history of every civilization — indeed, of every nation — includes one or more periods that seem to justify special designation. To use a figure of speech that is probably no longer as appropriate as it once was, each has its "Golden Age," some era distinguished by outstanding achievement — political, artistic, intellectual, material, or military, depending upon the sense of values of the historian.

It would be interesting to know how posterity will judge this age in which we live. We are witnessing the birth of a new civilization. What aspect of that civilization will future historians consider most significant? Will it be the almost unrecognized change that is taking place in our social and moral philosophy? Will it be our science? Or our industry? Will ours be remembered as the age that, through science and its applications, destroyed the dignity of and even the necessity for labor? Which will time declare the more important: our artificial satellites or the television programs we bounce off their uncomplaining antennas?

Any contemporary characterization of the present day in the face of the very complex transformations that are occurring can only be presumptive. I am no historian, so it is even presumptuous for me to suggest a designation for our age. But for purposes of this discussion, I should like to call it the Age of Research. Certainly it is the age in which man must begin to take seriously the study of himself and of his environment if he is to survive.

DISTINGUISHING FEATURES OF PAST AGES

Before we develop the spectrum of change that characterizes our new civilization, let us examine briefly some of the characteristics that distinguish historically significant ages of the past.

Certainly one such period occurred in the fourth and fifth centuries B.C., variously called the Golden Age of Greece or the Age of Pericles. A tremendous advance in historical theory would be achieved if we could analyze the factors that suddenly brought this remarkable period into being. The Greeks themselves had created their city-state. Politically, they were novices. They were doing everything for the first time. They had no experience and few material resources. They existed in a world of brutal warfare, slavery, human degradation — negations of the glorification of the human spirit that the Athens of Plato ultimately came to express. Historians call this the Age of Pericles, after the political ruler of the day. But Greece ruled the world then and has continued to rule it by the force of its intellectual attainments. This was the age of Plato and the beginnings of the democratic ideal.

It was also the day of Euclid and the incredible ordering of thought we call geometry. It was the day of Archimedes and the realization that physical phenomena could be comprehended as mental abstractions.

This period in the history of Greece is unique in the intensity and suddenness of its unfolding. Other ages in other lands seem somewhat trivial by comparison. The Napoleonic Period in European history calls to mind military campaigns that might have created a unified Europe 150 years ago if they had been as powerful intellectually as they were militarily. Dreams of military empire seem always to lead to disaster — a lesson all future aspirants for power based solely on force would do well to heed.

Several historically significant periods have been named for women. England has had two: the Elizabethan Era and the Victorian Age. Some may feel that the first might more accurately be designated Shakespearean, for it saw a sudden reawakening to the utility of the English language as a means for communicating ideas in a rapidly evolving culture. Indeed, more of Shakespeare than of Elizabeth survives in our present-day thought.

The characterization of the second of these English periods as Victorian undoubtedly carries romantic overtones. Those whose romance centers around science rather than women probably consider Maxwell's statement of the equations of the electromagnetic field far more important than anything Victoria accomplished; in their eyes, the period might more appropriately be designated Maxwellian. Clearly this is a matter of point of view.

The name Catherine is associated with a period in Russian

history, presumably for good and sufficient historical reasons. Here again, those whose interests lie in the realm of science will note that her reign saw Euler, the Swiss mathematician, leave his unhappy position at the court of Frederick the Great to join that of Catherine, who, as one historian has naively observed, "welcomed him with open arms." Whatever may have been intended by this display of cordiality, Euler's move did in fact shift the center of mathematical thought from Berlin to St. Petersburg and thereby significantly altered the course of world history.

It is unlikely that the present age will ever be named for any person — man or woman! Changes are occurring in too many diverse fields; no single individual can sufficiently influence them all to gain for himself so great an honor. Only a major prophet, whose enunciation of some new and universal principle resulted in unification of human thought and action throughout the world, could justifiably lend his name to this era.

THE INDUSTRIAL REVOLUTION: THE NEW CIVILIZATION

During the latter part of the eighteenth century, there began a sequence of changes referred to today as the Industrial Revolution. It involved quite simply the application of mechanical, chemical, and, somewhat later, electrical aids to industrial processes. The results were dramatic enough to characterize a period in history and to awaken in men's minds the vision of a world far more agreeable than any that had existed in the past. A concurrent transformation in political thinking suggested for the first time that everyone had a right to share in the "better life."

This electrifying and somewhat disturbing thought led on the one hand to certain of the idealistic political and social philosophies of those times. It led on the other hand to some pragmatic actions that realized human betterment in a very dramatic and material way. It led specifically to the modern industrial society, the benefits of which we currently enjoy in such abundance in the United States.

But what is going on in the world today is not a new Industrial Revolution. It is the birth of a *new civilization,* bringing in its wake changes in every facet of our existence — changes in order of magnitude greater than any that affected the factories and workers of the Industrial Revolution. What is happening today may, by oversimplification, be described as the sudden interaction of science and society. And the effects of this interaction transcend both science and society. Science appears to be the priming cap that has set off a social explosion.

We are witnessing the development of new standards in the arts. We are aware of a groping for a new morality. We find a revolution occurring in concepts of education, in methods of rearing children. We even see an important segment of the Christian Church willing to examine dogmas that have been traditional for hundreds of years — this in an attempt to solve the problems that today beset mankind. An age of such change represents no mere extension of the Industrial Revolution!

THE SPECTRUM OF CHANGE: THE NEW CIVILIZATION

It is not easy to grasp the entire significance of so broad a spectrum of change as we are witnessing. And characterization of this change as a spectrum is accurate: the problems involved are so interrelated that they cannot be separated; they grade insensibly one into the other.

Again at the risk of oversimplifying, we shall discuss this spectrum in terms of eight broad categories, describing for each some of the problems mankind must face in the new civilization — our so-called Age of Research.

Philosophical

The philosophical problems of any age become the focal point for the study of that age by philosophers in all the ages that follow. And quite naturally so! The philosophical problems that cause man concern — his destiny, the purpose of his existence, his religions, the collective purposes of the society in which he lives — are fundamental to everything he does.

A religious belief alone can affect the entire course of the development of a nation. In the Orient, for example, a religion that rejects the idea of killing animals for food interposes serious obstacles to the development of an economy such as ours, not because adequate nourishment cannot be obtained from vegetable sources, but because man must as a consequence take on the added burden of economic competition with the animals themselves. In the West, on the other hand, the permissiveness of Christianity has undoubtedly contributed to the freedom of economic development that we have enjoyed. Some may feel that Christianity has become *too* permissive, and this may be true; but it cannot be denied that there is a link between excessive religious restraint and economic inaction.

In today's civilization, the philosophical problems are no longer the concern solely of the philosopher; nor is religion the concern solely of the theologian. The new interest in syncretism and the vigorous ecumenical movement are evidence of a growing *popular* concern over such problems. We are becoming increasingly aware that they are relevant to all that we do, that they determine the basic fertility of the soil in which our institutions grow.

Scientific

Solutions to the scientific problems involved in man's relation to his environment are the goal of what we normally refer to as scientific research. Actually, this is a very loose concept. Science itself represents a wide spectrum of problems, ranging from those that are almost philosophical in nature to those that border on and eventually become indistinguishable from the technological. At the philosophical end is the work that is being done on the frontiers of knowledge. Mathematicians study the theory of categories, the structure of symbolic logic, topology, the peculiarities of the system of integers. Physicists seek a unified theory for the fields that describe the various phenomena of the physical world. Biologists investigate the nature of life and mechanisms of evolution, with results that quite clearly have philosophical and religious ramifications.

As scientific research moves from the theoretical to the practical, it undergoes continuous transition until it overlaps with technology. Many attempts have been made to assign precise definitions to basic, as opposed to applied, research. Such efforts would seem to serve no useful purpose, for here again a continuous spectrum is involved.

Technological

The technological problems to which applied research is directed are themselves extremely diversified in character. On the more scientific side, they may relate to the ultimate properties of materials and to the reasons that these properties are ultimate. Why is steel strong, for example, and why can't it be stronger?

There is a particularly definite scientific flavor in some of the problems of space technology. As we discover more and more about the nature of what was once called empty space, we draw ever more definite conclusions about cosmogony — which, in turn, borders on matters that are again philosophical.

In one technological area, that of water supply, problems of overwhelming importance are only beginning to receive the attention they have long required. Vast areas of the earth's land surface are presently desert; they need only water to make them productive. Even more pressing, perhaps, are the requirements of a modern urban civilization for an abundant supply of pure water. The availability of new energy sources promises to expedite the solution of these and a number of related problems.

Industrial

The problems of technology merge into those that are industrial. Technology is related to industry as thought is related to action. Technology must devise methods for the practical desalting of sea water. Industry must build and operate plants that can economically carry out the processes technology provides.

Economic

Industrial problems, then, are not entirely technological in nature. Somewhere along the spectrum, they merge with economic considerations. In our society, an industry must operate at a profit to survive — a boundary condition that raises problems of economy. But even in other societies, including those of the communist countries, economics cannot be ignored.

In our society, bad economic judgment is punished in extreme cases by bankruptcy, a somewhat messy but orderly process with overtones of social disapproval. In a communist society, bad economic judgment — even in one's personal affairs — is punished by the firing squad, by imprisonment, or by exile to a cold climate. In either society, the economic problems involved in man's relation to the physical world are controlling his struggle for existence.

Sociological

One often hears it stated that science — by which is meant physical science — is moving faster than ever before and leaving in its wake a transformed world. This is very probably true. But in our fascination with the progress of science we are apt to lose sight of the fact that the transformation itself is important. And nowhere are the changes occurring faster than in the sociological area.

Some of these changes are good and some are bad. It is well beyond the scope of this discussion to philosophize over why this is true or over what standards determine good or bad. We recognize certain benefits: from the greater productivity of the industrial machine; from the fact that less hard physical labor is required to run our new civilization; from the mechanization and consequent increased productivity of our agricultural community, which permit 10 per cent of the population to meet our present food requirements whereas this activity occupied 50 per cent of the population only a few decades ago.

Man doesn't have to work so hard to stay alive. He has a much greater variety of material benefits. Ease of communication has been increased. Man has acquired a perilous leisure.

These changes are producing profound reactions in sociological areas. The fact that man doesn't have to work so hard to earn a living has very complicated consequences. Work is considered honorable and dignified; but hard, exhausting labor is degrading. Between the two extremes there probably exists a happy medium, but we have yet to find it. Modern Western man is reacting to his new-found freedom from hard labor with joy — but a joy mingled with frustration, for he doesn't know quite what to do with this unaccustomed leisure.

In much the same way, the greater material benefits he enjoys have given man a new environment to control. He drives an automobile that for luxury and comfort would have inspired the envy of an emperor a few decades ago. But too often he fails to drive it responsibly.

Ease of communication has created in Western man an awareness of the rest of the world that has never before existed. And this is important, for the dream of a peaceful community of nations can only be realized if communication is complete and rapid. Now, for the first time, such communication is on man's horizon, extending even to those nations that are less technologically advanced.

Political

The political system under which we work and live has stood the pragmatic test of providing the abundant life we enjoy. We have recently chosen our national leaders for the next four years. We have exercised that really ultimate freedom, the freedom of choice — a freedom so all-inclusive that it does not even withhold from us, though perhaps it should, the right to reject freedom itself. It guarantees that we may continue to improve the society in which we live to whatever extent our knowledge allows, restricted only by our ability to apply that knowledge wisely. But if we would retain this freedom of choice, we must be prepared to meet the problems that go with it: the political problems of men who have chosen to govern themselves.

Personal

Personal problems round out our spectrum. They complete the octave. We are back again to problems philosophical — this time to the personal philosophy of each of us, to our individualistic outlook on the universe around us.

TRANSFORMATIONS IN PROGRESS

The spectrum of change described above may appear to be an extremely complicated representation of the problems that beset an industrial society. Actually, it is a simplification of the true picture. The changes involved are far more complex than the spectrum would indicate. Specialists are required within each individual area; but we must all attempt to grasp, if only vaguely, the picture as a whole.

The need for generalization is perhaps best illustrated by the number of transformations presently in progress that span broad segments of the spectrum. Let us look briefly at two examples.

The Increasing Social Responsibility of Industry

Any objective analyst of the nature of the communist threat must conclude that it can be met successfully only by offering to those who still have a freedom of choice something better than is offered by the communist system. It has been said that Karl Marx, writing when he did, could not have foreseen the graduated income tax and universal education. He could not have foreseen that the rapacity of capitalist exploitation could be controlled by law and even by the idealism of certain individual capitalists, whereas the rapacity of a dictatorship — and especially a dictatorship of the so-called proletariat — could never be brought under control once it was released. Similarly, the concept of the social responsibility of industry would not have been understood a century ago. Today it is taken for granted.

The modern technology-based corporation is a rapidly evolving institution of tremendous importance to the stability of Western culture. Within its corporate walls are found many of the elements of social organization for which men have been striving for decades. Men can spend their entire lives under its protection. Its program of social security is far more realistic than any the Government is likely to develop. It offers old age security and hospitalization protection to employees and their families. It offers paternalism to those who desire it. But more important, it offers ever greater opportunities for creative thought and action to those who have the necessary talents and wish to develop them. The competitive structure of our economy ensures to each individual the freedom to leave the shelter of one corporation and to seek that of another — or even to "go it alone" if he aspires to create a corporation of his own making.

Thus the industrial corporation operates over a broad segment of the spectrum of change we have outlined. The problems it encounters range from the scientific to the sociological — and not infrequently fall in the domain that is termed political.

The Advent of the Electronic Computer

The electronic computer bridges all segments of our spectrum of change, raising — and solving — problems in each. This remarkable development is based on a concept that had its origins in two almost philosophical areas, symbolic logic and the nature of thought; yet its influence extends to the opposite end of the spectrum, for it will eventually affect the personal lives of us all. One enthusiastic proponent has suggested that within twenty-five years every man in our country will have working for him the "computative" capacity of a hundred men — solving problems, we might add, before he even knows they exist.

The computer constitutes an amazing new tool for scientific research. Its own development engendered some excellent research in such fields as solid-state physics and pure mathematics. Its technology is important in its own right; it also provides the base on which some of the country's leading corporations are building their futures. It is transforming our approach to a number of economic problems and will almost certainly develop the only practicable solutions to many of them. Its sociological effects will derive from its tremendous potential as a decision maker and from its application in the field of automation. It will free the productive processes of industry from dependence on the labor of human hands and the thought of human minds. It will solve problems; it will create others.

You will forgive me if I speculate — perhaps a bit facetiously — about the possibilities of the computer in the political arena. We use a very high-sounding phrase to describe a certain aspect of our political philosophy: "Equal justice under law." Unfortunately, personal bias does on occasion pervert our sense of justice. Could a computer be built, capable of weighing legal evidence, making it possible to circumvent the factor of human error? The idea is not so farfetched as it might appear. The computer has already been introduced into the administrative machinery of the income tax, where it has taken over some of the functions of judge, jury, and executioner. Fearful as we may be of its merciless analysis, we must admit its impartiality.

Extension of this idea leads me to suggest the coinage of a new word, *cybernocracy,* meaning government by computer. Imagine, if you can, a computer sitting in the White House, optimizing the political well-being of each of us. We would continue to vote every four years — not for one program as opposed to another, but for or against a change of programming, and whether to the right or to the left. All of which leads logically to a fascinating concept that might be called *differential cybernocracy:* a state of political Nirvana where change is always possible but revolution impossible — unless someone pulls the plug on the computer!

THE PROBLEM OF LEISURE

After so light-hearted a treatment of the computer, permit me to return to a subject that is far from humorous. Our increased productivity and our changing ideas with respect to equity of distribution of the world's material wealth confront us with a serious problem: What is man to do with the time he once spent making a living? How is he to utilize his new leisure?

Perhaps we shall find this the most difficult of all our problems. It has tragic potentialities if answers are not found. At the philosophical end of the spectrum it involves us collectively in questions concerning the destiny of man, the purpose of his existence. At the other end it poses the same questions to each of us personally. Moreover, the potential sociological and political effects are ominous. Leisure offers to some the possibility of following pleasurable and creative pursuits — of enriching their lives. But it confronts society as a whole with such phenomena as teenage groups who murder for no other reason than that they are bored. One may suggest paradoxically that the only solution to a boring leisure is useful work. But it is not obvious what such work should be.

The picture I have attempted to draw is that of a world of human beings beset by problems in every area of their existence. The problems are complex. Some are unbelievably difficult. But all must be solved using the best tools that man can find, or they will solve themselves through the inexorable forces of nature. In past geological ages these forces have exterminated biological species that refused to adapt to an environment or to meet its challenge by changing it.

There come to mind the oft-quoted lines of Alexander Pope:

> *Know then thyself, presume not God to scan;*
> *The proper study of mankind is Man.*

There is a real hope that the research carried on so enthusiastically and effectively on such projects as the conquest of space will be extended to other areas. Whether posterity calls it so or not, this *must* be the Age of Research. It is time that man really began in earnest the study of himself. And beyond the fact that the study will go on in specific detail in university, corporation, and institute laboratories, the world itself must recognize that it has become a laboratory where actions in one domain affect deeply and inevitably reactions in another. If we pursue our studies diligently, I think we shall find that we are indeed intimately involved in the birth of a new civilization. Hopefully, we may even come to enjoy some of the satisfactions that reward successful parenthood.

Federal Support of
Science and Technology

R. L. Sproull
Director, Advanced Research Projects Agency
United States Department of Defense

The interaction between the United States Government and our national scientific effort is a marvelously complicated one. I should like to discuss only one of its many aspects: the Federal program of financial support for science and technology. This remarkably successful program has had a significant effect on the civilian economy and is now the subject of close public scrutiny. We shall do well, then, to look at its contributions to date and to examine problems involved in its future administration.

At the outset, let me emphasize that these problems are in no sense desperate. They constitute no crisis. But we do handle some better than we handle others. There are areas where innovation and experimentation are definitely called for. There are other areas to which we can point with justifiable pride.

SCIENCE AND TECHNOLOGY IN THE PUBLIC EYE
Unusual public attention has been focused on Federal research and

development support within the last year or two. The Elliott [1] and Daddario [2] Committees of Congress have studied it systematically. The President's Science Advisory Committee and the National Science Foundation have intensified their studies — in fields ranging from coal utilization to high-energy physics. The National Academy of Sciences and many professional societies have responded with more than routine motion.

A number of factors are responsible for this increased interest.

There is a growing conviction that the spending rate for science and technology cannot continue to grow exponentially, that it must soon exhibit an S-shaped growth-curve behavior. But when? And at what level?

The apparent saturation in Federal spending rates is another important factor. Growth since the war has consisted of a series of step functions: As each new agency has entered the scene, its budget has soon saturated — at least on a man-year basis, and usually on a dollar basis as well. The sum of all such step functions, each with a different starting time, closely resembles a continuous, rapid, almost exponential growth. The latest major contribution is NASA, now six years old and unmistakably saturating. Where is the next increment to originate?

A deterioration in the competitive position of science-based American industry in world markets is also the source of some anxiety. The thought has been expressed that United States science and technology are bearing the major burden of the military research and development required for the defense of the Free World, and meanwhile other Western nations assign so much of their resources to industrial research and development that our competitive market position is deteriorating. Ought we to allocate more effort to nonspace, nondefense research and development? How can the Federal Government help?

The various regions of the United States have in the past based their industry largely on their differing natural resources — mineral deposits, arable land, climate, access to world markets. Regional leaders have quite generally accepted the facts of competitive life. Science-based industry, on the other hand, can locate anywhere. Now each region wants its own "instant MIT," complete with Route 128. What should the strategy be for the regional distribution of Federal funds for science and technology?

The importance of Federal research funds to university programs of higher education, especially graduate education, is becoming more and more apparent. It has been estimated that Federal support of university research must grow at the rate of 15 per cent per year to accommodate the inflation of costs and the increasing numbers of graduate students. The American public is probably more concerned than ever before about the quality and adequacy of graduate training. Will Federal support keep pace?

Following World War II, American universities underwent tremendous changes in size, in structure, and in emphasis. Are similar changes, especially in engineering, now necessary to keep technical education responsive to the opportunities and needs of the present? What principles should set the size of the whole university effort?

Finally, the attitude of the public toward science — which

approached mystic reverence at the end of World War II — has changed markedly, though probably predictably. The layman's awed respect has often been replaced by an attitude of "What has science done *for me, today?*" The result: an increased attention to the strategy of Federal spending in support of scientific research.

SUCCESS STORIES

In the face of this closer scrutiny of science, frequently by jaundiced eyes, we ought to remind ourselves that the postwar interaction between the United States Government and our industrial and academic scientific community has been remarkably successful. This success can sometimes even be measured quantitatively, in such terms as Nobel prizes and aircraft Mach numbers.

Much of the credit, as I see it, should go to what might be called the "ONR tradition." At the end of the war, a small group in the Office of Naval Research transferred the wartime NDRC–OSRD experience to a peacetime setting. [3] They developed the pattern of unclassified contracts, negotiated by technical people with technical people, monitored with official restraint and a minimum of reporting, and defended in Washington in terms of long-term advances of relevant science and technology rather than in terms of immediate applications to military problems. As other agencies entered the contract research field, they adopted the basic principles of the ONR tradition.

The many case histories that give testimony to the success of postwar Federal support of science are well known. High-energy physics was created. A new, richer spectroscopy of gases and solids led to the maser and the laser. Astrophysics was stimulated. Radioastronomy was expanded from a single observation to a major field. Space explorations were begun. Selenography was made an acceptable science. The list is all but endless.

Postwar successes in technology — defined as research and development applied to the creation of new products or processes or to the improvement of old ones — are equally numerous and have been far more obvious to the layman. Here, of course, the partnership with industry has been necessarily close, and the credit must be shared. Nuclear reactors, including submarine- and ship-borne reactors, have reached a high state of sophistication. Central-station power reactors are approaching the capital cost of $100 per kilowatt-hour of capacity and the comparably low fuel costs that will make them competitive with "conventional" — perhaps soon to be called "unconventional" — electric power generators. Versatile aircraft have been developed: some capable of Mach-2.5 dash and yet a 125-knot landing speed, others with gross take-off weights of half a million pounds. New military systems have been developed, including Polaris, Minuteman, and frightfully ingenious guidance devices owing much to the solid-state device technology almost unknown before 1948.

I might add parenthetically that Federal administration of research funds should be judged by what has *not* been supported as well as by what *has*. Early ONR leaders had the vision to provide funds for helium liquefiers at many universities, thereby helping to establish U.S. eminence in the field of low-temperature physics. This success prompted hardware-oriented people to suggest that Federal support go to create a *field* of high-temperature physics as well. There are many interesting and important investigations to be done at high temperatures, but a strategy of support of a *field* as such is made less promising by the diversity of phenomena: electric behavior of plasmas, radiation, phase changes, excited states, chemical reactions, etc. It was decided, therefore, to support low-temperature but not high-temperature physics *as a field of science* — an example of one of the wise exercises of choice that have been made.

This is not to say that high-temperature research has received no Federal support. Both high- and low-temperature investigations have been energetically encouraged. They are, in fact, typical of a general theme that characterizes Federal support of science and technology: the invasion of new regimes — extremely high or extremely low temperatures, high pressures, high magnetic fields, high velocities, other extreme conditions. From the scientific standpoint, investigations in such extreme regimes create the possibility of observing new phenomena and generating new theoretical understanding. From the technological standpoint, they challenge instrumentation and even manufacturing methods and permit new generations of devices.

The successes of the past are, of course, not necessarily relevant today. What we are interested in now is the best method of administering science and technology in the future, not in methods that worked moderately well in the past. World War II experience, in particular, probably has nothing further to contribute: all its value has already been incorporated into the system. The "crash" engineering programs of 1939 to 1945, in which virtually all U.S. scientists and many of Europe's best participated, were eminently successful in exploiting science in certain definite directions, when no need to exploit science in these particular directions had existed earlier. But this tells us nothing about how scientists and engineers should behave in 1965.

TWO MYTHS AND SOME SPILLOVER

As we look ahead, it seems to me that we must dispose of two myths. The first is that basic research is a fruit tree: you shake the tree, and new products and technology come showering down. The relationship between basic research and technological innovation is actually much more complicated. More often than not, invention is required, usually by people who are not creative scientists. I shall return to this point in the next section.

The second myth is that applied research and development — for defense, for space exploration, or for any other specific mission — is a fruit tree: you shake the tree, and new products and technology for quite different purposes come showering down. It cannot be denied that this frequently happens. The myth lies only in the belief that it happens automatically and efficiently. Of course the military KC-135 becomes the civilian Boeing 707. Of course improvements in the internal combustion engine benefit civilian industry even if the work is done for military trucks. But most Department of Defense, NASA, and AEC research and development is by no means so directly applicable to nonmilitary scientific progress. It would indeed be a cynical comment on management to assert that a million dollars spent on a lunar landing vehicle would contribute as much to the development of new nonspace products as would a million dollars directed specifically toward the latter goal.[4]

Thus the benefits that accrue to American industry and to the American consumer as a result of these large applied military and space programs can be only a fraction — and usually a very small fraction — of the benefits the same expenditures could have produced if focused directly on civilian technology. And as the management of these large programs continues to improve, the "spillover" or "fallout" for the civilian economy may become even less, since better management will accomplish the specific research and development mission with less peripheral expense.

PROBLEM AREAS

I have said that the interaction between the United States Government and our national scientific and technological effort is a marvelously complicated one. Let us look now at some of the specific problems that lie within the area of that interaction. We shall consider in sequence issues that relate most directly to science, then to technology, and finally to industrial and Governmental organization.

Science for Science's Sake

Certainly some science ought to be supported simply for its own intrinsic value as one of the great enterprises of Western civilization, innocent of and uncontaminated by thought of application. The question is: How much? And how should such support be distributed among the various fields of science?

One answer that has been suggested: Support all promising scientists. As day-to-day guidance this approach may be useful. But it is clearly not applicable over years or decades, since there is a kind of Parkinson's law of graduate research: Graduate students expand to consume the available support. Control of the availability of fellowships and even of science emphasis in high schools also defeats this approach. Finally, how does one define "promising"? One might as well try to administer a national policy of supporting all "promising" musicians!

Another answer that has been proposed: Ours is a rich country, with a large and growing gap between the total work effort expended and the effort that is needed just to survive at the subsistence level; more and more of that gap should be devoted to supporting the arts and sciences. This approach is better, but it is not quantitative — unless one goes to the extreme, as does the young academic politician in F. M. Cornford's *Microcosmographia Academica* who simply wants "all the money there is going"!

Professor R. R. Wilson has called synchrotrons "the cathedrals of the twentieth century." This comparison has its points, but it has a serious defect: Even Quasimodo experienced a feeling of exaltation in Notre Dame de Paris; few nonscientists feel anything at all about science, and those who do probably feel awe mixed with suspicion rather than loyalty or participation.

Nevertheless, there may be a useful basis for the support of pure science in this premise. Approached from this point of view, science for science's sake would be supported by local and state governments as well as by the Federal Government and would compete for public favor with monuments, parks, sports, and the flickering screen. The amount of this support would obviously be contingent upon a feeling of public pride and participation — a feeling that would in turn require major changes in elementary and high school education aimed toward increasing general scientific awareness. Science writing and reporting could also help, but only if the aim were to *inform* rather than to *impress;* the public is probably quickly saturated with the "Gee, whiz!" type of science reporting.

I do not know how much pure science could be supported under such an approach, and it seems a little unimaginative to tie the size of science to the quality of science writing rather than to opportunities for discovery. But the system offers some advantages over the frequent practice of justifying pure science by hinting darkly that great new technology will come out of *all* science — even in such fields as cosmology. Such practice is writing blank checks that will eventually be cashed. In the case of high-energy physics, the cashing has already been threatened.

Incidentally, there is no theorem that states that all discoveries must be made in this century.

Science for science's sake is obviously best pursued in university laboratories or in foundation laboratories like the Institute for Advanced Study. I see very little justification for Federal support of science under this banner in industrial or Government laboratories.

As for distribution of funds among the various fields, this task could probably be handled most effectively by an organization such as the National Academy of Sciences. Although the members of that distinguished body do not now devote enough time to its affairs to take on this responsibility, perhaps the tradition could develop that acceptance of Academy membership carried the obligation of full-time service in Washington for at least a year.

Science for Teaching's Sake

Some science ought to be supported for its essential role in university instruction. Undergraduate science and engineering instruction demands instructors who are simultaneously creating new knowledge, the only known way of staying "scientifically alive." The size of this sector of scientific activity is obviously determined by the size of undergraduate enrollments and the popularity of scientific subjects.

Undergraduate demand for technical courses will, I hope, grow faster than undergraduate enrollment. We are still turning out millions of scientifically and mathematically illiterate B.A.'s each year. Calculus is one of the great achievements of all time; its basic ideas lend themselves to intimate and detailed application in daily life. Yet most university graduates are untainted by the foggiest notion of what mathematics is all about: they are completely lost, for example, in elementary probability theory.

Society would be the richer if scientific illiteracy were abolished among college graduates. The country would be the stronger if science majors were being graduated "in surplus," so that after the strict needs of the profession were met some would still be available to enter public life as English and Government majors now do. Federal — and, one hopes, state and local — support of science in the universities must somehow be expanded to provide the additional instruction by active research scientists that these objectives demand.

Science for Technology's Sake

The rationale of the size and the mechanism of support of science for technology's sake are probably the problems most germane to this symposium; they are also the most difficult to solve. There is no serious questioning of the support of science for this purpose, only of the amount. As I have already suggested, some science that should have been justified for its own sake has crept under this banner, with consequences not yet fully evaluated but possibly damaging.

In the large, mission-oriented Government agencies, support of pure science almost always accompanies support of applications and engineering development. In the Department of Defense, for example, research accounts for about 6 per cent and exploratory development for about 17 per cent of the total Research, Development, Test, and Evaluation budget. Each individual area — such as night vision or rocket propellants — is periodically scrutinized thoroughly, and this balance between exploration and product development in each area makes sense. Thus the distribution in over-all figures must be reasonably appropriate. I believe the distribution between basic exploration and applications in other agencies and in industrial practice is not much different. As one proceeds from the general (e.g., the laser concept) to a specific application (e.g., a Raman laser using a particular compound for a particular application), much more effort is required to be sure the right product is being developed in the best way. Development thus costs more than the research underlying it.

If we accept the assignment of one dollar of basic, scientifically oriented exploration to each four or five dollars of product development, we have a workable rationale for the size of technology-connected science. (Note that the size of this program may in turn affect the amount of support required for university research, since it is in the universities that any additional scientists and engineers necessary to progressive technology must be trained.) As technology grows more complex, the basic research fraction may have to grow, but generally the distribution seems sensible, and I see no great issues here.

There are many problems in laboratory management, however. For example, the best conditions for invention and for harvesting basic research are not known, though much is known about them. Certainly one element is recognition of the inventor as an innovator comparable in stature to the scientist. Another is probably creating an appreciation by the scientist of the connections between his work and possible technologies. Pertinent to this problem, Dr. Chalmers Sherwin has initiated a promising study of the conditions under which significant advances in military technology have been made. He is attempting to identify the key developments that made possible such systems as Polaris and is asking about each: Where was the work done? Under what kind of management was the work completed? How was the work supported?

Another problem originates in the scenario that runs as follows: A company creates a research laboratory — for a variety of good reasons plus the desire for prestige and a visceral feeling that no matter what research is done or how it is done, it will somehow prove useful. Academically oriented scientists are attracted by promises of undirected research opportunities. They arrive and proceed to rework their Ph.D. theses. Eventually the company discovers that all this costs money and, if of benefit to anybody, is of greatest benefit to its competitors since the company has not mastered the subtle art of connecting science to technology. At this point, one should expect an appeal for Government research funds.

To return to the more typical problem, the Defense Science Board is currently studying various possible innovations in the administration of industrial research and development support with a view to improving the creativity of contractors. Although it is too early to predict their findings, their efforts are indicative of the concern for and attention to the effect of Federal funds on industrial research and development.

Training for Connecting Science and Technology
Since World War II, there have been only two periods of comparative balance between the supply of and the demand for

scientists and engineers: that just preceding the Korean War and the present. At all other times, there has been a "seller's market." This circumstance is heartily enjoyed by the individuals in such a market, but it has had unfortunate consequences. Laboratories have hired Ph.D.'s who have "just barely made it" to do undirected research under only remote supervision. The graduate student was not forced to think deeply about where he could make his greatest contribution to his own welfare and to that of society. He knew that he would be offered a choice of jobs, any one of which would allow him to continue the basic research he had been led to enjoy at the university.

The present closer balance between supply and demand should give us an important opportunity. It should be possible to attract the student's attention earlier to his choice of career and his approach to his life's work. I hope that more science students will, in Harvey Brooks' words, "acquire a respect for applied problems" in the course of their university training. Ideally, some of the ablest may then be attracted to Government and industrial laboratories who openly and honestly describe the work they offer as partly pure, partly applied, but always relevant to the employer's goals. The opportunities are virtually unlimited for young men — as often as not Ph.D.'s in science — to establish new and imaginative connections between science and technology.

It is unfortunate that, just when more capable people are becoming available to less well-known employers, many industrial and Government laboratories are not in the market, either because of restrictions placed upon them or because of a slightly panicky feeling that the supply-demand change itself has engendered. Strangely enough, a company that lavishes executive thought and computer analysis down to the last penny on the price it pays for steel frequently seems content with buying only at the top of the market the one "commodity" — technical people — that more than any other determines the company's future.

Nevertheless, the closing gap between supply and demand does provide hope that abler people will ultimately be available to attack the rate-limiting problems in technology.

Government Support and University Structure

One of the most rewarding features of the ONR tradition is its support of individual university scientists or small university groups through contracts negotiated by technical people on both sides. Because individual scientists, rather than academic administrators, have brought the contracts and grants to the universities, research support has enjoyed a quasi-independence from the institutional structure of departments and colleges. Of course, local coordination is necessary for allocation of space, interaction with teaching responsibilities, preservation of the quality and role appropriate to the university, and the like. But the promising individual research worker can be supported even in a poor department, and a group of professors from different departments can receive support for a common program.

Institutional as opposed to project Government support is becoming more prominent, and I believe that the trend is desirable. Universities need flexibility to create large facilities and to make the whole greater than the sum of its parts. But I should heartily deplore the withering of support for the individual professor, since it facilitates the crossing of academic department boundaries and protects against institutional arteriosclerosis. American universities have long looked wistfully at the British University Grants Committee system, and their five-year institutional support grants would be a welcome addition to the American scene. But it is worth noting that even at Oxbridge the freedom that a U.S. Defense contract gives to a young researcher is highly prized.

Our present system, then, is not without merit. Still, experimentation is very welcome. We shall do well to follow closely such promising innovations as the Research Career Awards Program of the National Institutes of Health.

Cost and Spillover

I have referred previously to the spillover that accrues to the civilian economy from the research programs of the big three: defense, space, and atomic energy. Is there any way in which this spillover can be made more effective?

I doubt it. Management of these programs focuses funds with ever-increasing precision on each specific mission, and that mission is not the stimulation of American industry. Furthermore, consumer-oriented industry operates in an entirely different cost regime than do programs of the big three. The cost per pound for space vehicles — minus fuel — is greater than the cost per pound of one-hundred-dollar watches. Airframes and nuclear fuels are only a little less expensive. The technology of these advanced systems cannot be expected to contribute much to the technology of the building industry or even, with a few exceptions, of the automotive industry — in fact, to the technology of just about any industry other than one-hundred-dollar watches. The funds simply go into different activities: In each of the VELA nuclear test detection satellites, for example, 40,000 electronic elements have worked in space for over a year, which implies fantastic mean-times-to-failure of individual components. The technology of producing this amazing reliability has very little to contribute to making a twenty-dollar automatic washer timer survive for more than six months.

Government Stimulation of Industrial Research and Development
If the spillover or fallout route is not efficient, how can the Federal Government be helpful in industrial growth? I have no comfortable or complete answer, but I should like to propose some possibly uncomfortable and certainly partial answers.

In the common market countries, commercial research and development represents a larger fraction of their total research and development — though a smaller percentage of gross national product — than in the United States, and the proportion is rapidly increasing. The former Assistant Secretary of the Army for Research and Development, Dr. Richard S. Morse, has testified before a Senate Subcommittee that Japan and Germany have nearly twice as many people as we do per 100,000 population working on commercial research and development.[5] Clearly our competitive position abroad as well as growth at home depends on finding ways to bring additional research and development to bear efficiently on new products, product improvement, and cost reduction.

Large companies, while of course restricted by total earnings, can distribute part of their earnings to research and development. Their size gives them the ability to set up laboratories adequately larger than the threshold size for effectiveness. But much of nonspace, nondefense industry is dispersed in a large number of *small* companies that cannot maintain laboratories large enough to be productive and intellectually attractive.

Consider, for example, a comparison of the missile industry and the building industry. The missile industry is concentrated in a few large companies. Its products have a value of many dollars per pound. Transportation and marketing present no problems. Raw materials are standardized. Competition centers around performance, innovations, and delivery times. The greatest concerns of the customer — the United States Government — are quality and reliability, and for these he will pay whatever price is necessary. The building industry, on the other hand, is dispersed in many small companies. Its products have a value of relatively few dollars per pound. Transportation and marketing present controlling problems. Raw materials vary. The greatest concern of the customer, who has no performance-testing capability, is price; the producer must develop for himself an awareness of quality requirements.

Much of civilian industry, like the building industry, is intermediate in size and character between a large, highly technical company and a small family farm. This circumstance has prompted Dr. J. Herbert Hollomon and others to propose an extension service to bring university skills to bear on small company research and development. Another possibility, which I think might be even more effective, is the enlarging and strengthening of the concept of industry research and development institutes, such as the Textile Research Institute at Princeton. Such institutes can help a dispersed industry bootstrap its way into new products, but their total size is now wholly inadequate in comparison with the size of the opportunity. Eighty per cent of all research and development in the United States today is done by 300 companies. Forty per cent of the total effort is concentrated in the aerospace, electrical-electronic, and chemical fields. There is room for spectacular growth of research and development in the other industries.

But how can Government funds be brought to bear? "It is easy to propose impossible solutions," as Aesop said, going on to ask: "Who is to bell the cat?" I doubt if additional Government laboratories (following the U.S. Department of Agriculture pattern) are the answer. Perhaps if *all* industry associations would create viable research and development institutes, the provision of Federal funds through grants or tax concessions would be more palatable.

Both the small companies and the large should benefit from the increased supply of technically trained people, especially if

through long-term budgeting (like the Ford Scientific Laboratory's five-year budget) they can take advantage of a steady
supply accompanied by fluctuations in the demand.

Science and Technology Information

It would indeed be unfashionable not to include the handling
of technical information among the problem areas of science and
technology. It is well known that the conservative technical
societies have failed to keep pace in this field with the needs. A
recent President's Science Advisory Committee panel thoroughly
analyzed the problem and described some elements of its solution.[6]
Their study focused attention on the need for critically evaluated
information and on the role information centers should play —
centers where the orderly assembly of new information is carried
out by technical people who themselves are creating new information. Many such centers are already in operation, and new
additions like the large National Bureau of Standards Standard
Reference Data Program are most promising.

Nevertheless, there is much more to do here. The new developments in the way men interact with computers and in "list
structures" in computer stores open up remarkable possibilities.
Instead of asking for *information* on titanium, for example, and
having hundreds of pounds of *documents* descend, one can now
conceive of a conversation with the computer in which it feels out
his interest and sharpens his specification of what will be useful.
Government sponsorship of the orderly, responsive handling of
technical information could turn out to be second in importance

only to Government sponsorship of graduate training as an aid to industrial research and development.

The Partnership

The administrator in Washington and the scientist or engineer supported through his efforts are partners in creating science and technology. Yet the relationship between them seems often to assume tug-of-war characteristics. Since I represent the Government side of the partnership, I am well stocked with advice for the other side.

Most important of all, perhaps, let me point out that it is the bench scientist or engineer who has all the fun. The administrator must gain his pleasure, if any, vicariously. The pleasure is rare, as the following example will show: There is a Government committee on materials research and development that meets once a month. It is composed of people whose programs total about two hundred million dollars per year. That is, they support some four thousand senior scientists and engineers. If we define an "outstanding idea" or a "remarkable discovery" as an idea or discovery that is the *most important* idea or discovery a professional man has in his lifetime, then this committee should hear about (on the average) *eight* once-in-a-lifetime developments each month! In fact, of course, the committee is lucky if it learns of one.

Real discoveries — not just reasons for needing more money — can be briefly and promptly described to the man at the source of funds, with benefit for all. If the recipient of the funds does not believe the administrator will be interested in, or can understand the significance of, the new development, there is a serious question in my mind as to whether he should accept the support. Acceptance of money under such circumstances may or may not be degrading, but it is certainly unstable.

This brings me to another aspect of this partnership. Universities and other recipients of research and development funds should recognize the obligation to give or lend some of their most capable people for service in Washington. More is required than passive acquiescence. An institution must be willing to tell one of its most valued employees that service in Washington will aid the institution and the career of the individual in the institution.

Another aspect of the partnership is the responsibility of the individual recipient to keep himself informed on how his work is represented and defended through the Federal budget process and to the Congress. It may happen, for example, that a certain basic research program is defended as imminently applicable to a practical problem. The fund recipient who does not agree that this defense is justified is faced with three choices: He can suggest a change in strategy, accepting the risk that funds will be cut as a result; he can apply to a different agency for support; or he can do nothing, accepting the risk that a "day of reckoning" will eventually come. If he chooses the third course, he forfeits any right to cry "Foul!" or to weep crocodile tears should the program and his part in it be cut after the best efforts of the agency program manager fail.

Having passed along this advice, I should add that quite generally a joint sense of responsibility and satisfaction is enjoyed by both grantor and grantee. Not infrequently, dialogue between the two is active, permitting each to feel out the problems and opportunities of the other.

And so I end as I began. We face no crisis in this matter of Government support for science and technology. There are possibilities for trouble that we must watch with care, but there is much in the program of which we can be proud. There are promising innovations to be tried. There is also room for the kind of openminded, risk-taking experimentation that characterizes our scientific tradition.

[1] Select Committee on Government Research, House of Representatives, 88th Congress (Hearings, 1963, 1964; ten staff studies, late 1964).

[2] Subcommittee on Science, Research, and Development of the Committee on Science and Astronautics, House of Representatives, 88th Congress (Hearings, 1963, 1964; five reports, 1964).

[3] See "The Evolution of the Office of Naval Research," *Physics Today*, **14** (No. 8), 30 (1961).

[4] See Hearings of the Elliott and Daddario House Committees already cited (footnotes 1 and 2, respectively); see also Hearings of the Subcommittee on Retailing, Distribution, and Marketing Practices (Senator Hubert H. Humphrey, Chairman) of the Select Committee on Small Business, U.S. Senate, 88th Congress (Hearings, 1963).

[5] Richard S. Morse, Hearings before the Subcommittee on Retailing, Distribution, and Marketing Practices of the Select Committee on Small Business, "A Review of the Effect of Government Research and Development on Economic Growth," p. 194 (June 5-6, 1963).

[6] See "Science, Government, and Information: The Responsibilities of the Technical Community and the Government in the Transfer of Information," Report of the President's Science Advisory Committee, January 10, 1963.

Basic Research in the Industrial Laboratory

John Bardeen
Professor of Physics, University of Illinois

It is a fact of economic life that our large government and industrial laboratories are dedicated to programs of mission-directed applied research and engineering development. It is less well known that these same laboratories also support substantial programs of basic research. They employ some of the world's outstanding scientists in such areas as solid-state physics, for example, and allow them to publish their experimental results freely.

Why? What prompts industry to carry on basic research? The hope for unexpected breakthroughs? Perhaps. But more important are the less direct benefits that ultimately accrue to its applied research and development programs. Before examining more closely the nature of these benefits and the organizational factors that maximize them, permit me a few brief comments on scientific research in general.

Basic research is defined by the National Science Foundation as that directed toward fuller knowledge and understanding rather than toward practical application.[1] I prefer not to stress the last phrase of this definition, since I believe that much good basic research is done with applications in mind.

Basic scientific research is enjoying a period of unprecedented growth and activity. In terms of money spent, numbers of people involved, technical publications — and also, I believe, in terms of real accomplishments — science is flourishing as never before. This is no mere amassing of more detailed data in old areas of interest. Whole new areas of understanding are opening up in such fields as high-energy physics, molecular biology, radio-astronomy, solid-state physics, and the space sciences.

CONTEMPORARY SCIENCE AND TECHNOLOGY

High-Energy Physics

No one knew quite what to expect when a new generation of particle accelerators came into operation a few years ago. High-energy physicists discovered to their surprise the existence of a host of short-lived particles or resonances never before observed. At first, these particles seemed to fall into no recognizable patterns. Very recently, however, research has disclosed an underlying symmetry that has enabled physicists to establish relationships between the masses and even to predict new particles. As yet, the exact nature of these symmetries and the reasons for their existence remain a mystery.

Molecular Biology

Many feel that molecular biology will occupy the center of the scientific stage during the next half century. There is now a rational basis for understanding a number of biological processes at the atomic level. Advances have been made, based largely on new knowledge of the chemical structures and functions of DNA (desoxyribonucleic acid) and RNA (ribonucleic acid). Very important to progress in this field has been the work accomplished at Cambridge and Oxford on the analysis of protein structure by x-ray crystallography, a task made immensely difficult by the thousands of atoms that compose a protein molecule. Nobel prizes in chemistry, awarded in 1962 to J. C. Kendrew and M. F. Perutz for their work on the structures of myoglobin and hemoglobin and in 1964 to Dorothy Hodgkin for her pioneering work on the structure of complex organic molecules, testify eloquently to the significance of their activities. It is interesting to note that it took Perutz twenty-two years to resolve the structure of hemoglobin. Obviously, the enormous amounts of time and effort sometimes required to solve really difficult but worthwhile problems are well rewarded. Also exemplified here is the interdependence of scientific advances: structural investigations of such complex organic molecules could hardly have succeeded without new techniques of x-ray crystallography and the aid of large digital computers.

PUBLIC SUPPORT OF SCIENCE AND TECHNOLOGY

Science for Its Own Sake

High-energy physics, molecular biology, and the other fields we have mentioned are among the most exciting in science today.

And they require increasingly large expenditures of funds for their support. Understanding the world in which we live is one of the highest aspirations of mankind; on this basis, science can be justified and should be supported for its own sake. In practice, however, the amount of government and philanthropic support science can expect from society is necessarily limited. Society is more strongly motivated to support research by its expectation of such practical benefits as have resulted from occasional, usually unanticipated breakthroughs in the past: atomic energy, antibiotics, computer technology, semiconductor electronics. Of more recent vintage are the maser and the laser, for the development of which C. H. Townes and two Soviet physicists were awarded the 1964 Nobel prize in physics. To what extent the public *ought* to support so exciting but expensive a field as high-energy physics, where expectations of direct practical benefit are small, is a question upon which we shall not dwell.

Impact of Technology on Science
Looking back, it is interesting to note how much of contemporary science and technology was stimulated by research done for very practical goals during World War II. The ramifications of atomic energy development are well known. Perhaps not so widely recognized are the outgrowths of research on radar, with its techniques for work with microwaves: magnetic resonance, now used extensively in both physics and chemistry; radioastronomy; the discovery of the maser. The advance in our knowledge of semiconductors is based largely on research into the properties

of silicon and germanium, each of which was subject to intensive study for application in the area of radar detection during the war.

SOME ASPECTS OF BASIC RESEARCH IN INDUSTRY

Indirect Benefits

We have already stated that the main goal of basic industrial research is not a scientific breakthrough that will lead to new products. Rather, it is a better understanding of the processes and methods in which the company has vested interests. Basic research reduces empiricism, points out intrinsic limitations, indicates directions in which progress is possible. Those engaged in basic research serve as an important channel of communication with the scientific world. By interacting with those concerned more directly with applied research and development, they help to improve the over-all quality of the work. And there is a feedback in the other direction as well: interesting basic problems are not infrequently suggested by those working in applied areas.

Freedom But Not Isolation

I feel that a group doing basic research cannot live long in isolation; it should be associated either with graduate teaching in the university or with applied research in industrial and government laboratories. Not only are the indirect benefits enumerated above lost if the group is isolated, but the basic research itself suffers after a period of time from lack of adequate stimulation. Even such a renowned organization as the Rockefeller Institute found it necessary to go into graduate teaching in order to survive.

Obviously, then, basic research groups in industry should not be isolated from those working on applied research and engineering development. They should be well aware of their company's immediate problems and goals. On the other hand, they should be free to work on long-range problems, with limited demands made on their time for trouble-shooting when difficulties arise in other areas.

Field Selectivity

Fields of basic research within an industrial laboratory must be carefully and selectively chosen. If the effort is spread too thin, little progress will be made in any area. Token interest in certain fields may serve the useful purpose of keeping the company in touch with progress of potential value in those fields. But in areas vital to the development of the company, research groups should be sufficiently strong to rank among the leaders. A group of sub-critical size or ability — lacking a position at the forefront of its activity — is of no great value.

Industrial Capability

Only a few industrial organizations are of sufficient size and stature to profit from programs of basic research. Xerox is perhaps the newest on the scene. Not only must the company be large and financially strong; it must have sufficient command of its markets to be able to introduce innovations and to profit from them. Unfortunately, many of our industries are too fragmented for any one company to introduce revolutionary changes in practice. The building industry, as Dr. Sproull points out, is a prime example.

Two factors are involved in innovation or invention: recognition of a need, and provision of the technical means for filling that need. In some cases, one factor predominates, in some cases, the other; often elements of both are important. The genius of many inventors of the past century has been that they recognized a need, saw a better way of doing things, and then found the technical means to put their ideas into effect. I would place Chester Carlson in this class, even though considerable technological development was required to make practical his invention of xerography; his dream of more than 25 years ago has seen full fruition only during the last few years. In the case of the transistor, the need was recognized but a breakthrough in scientific understanding was required to accomplish the goal of making a semiconductor amplify electric signals without the use of a heated filament. I have already called attention to cases where innovation arose solely from new scientific discoveries. On those rare occasions when a scientific breakthrough is made, one naturally looks for possible applications; where feasible, attempts are made to exploit the breakthrough in terms of salable products. And those companies that carry on advanced research programs of their own are in the best position to take advantage of basic scientific discoveries wherever in the world they may occur.

I have been fortunate enough to watch at fairly close hand

three fields that have undergone rapid development and expansion during the last ten or fifteen years: semiconductor electronics, xerography, and superconductivity. The first two have had a large economic impact. It is too early to predict the practical consequences of superconductivity, but almost certainly they will not be as great, at least for many years. Since basic research has played quite a different role in each of these three cases, it might be worthwhile to review their individual histories.

Semiconductor Electronics

The transistor is one of the exceptional cases where invention resulted from a program of basic research. After the war, at the instigation of Mervin Kelly, William Shockley, and others, a new research program on various aspects of solid-state physics was initiated at the Bell Telephone Laboratories. The fields chosen — semiconductors, magnetism, and dielectrics — were those of potential interest to the company. A long-range goal of the semiconductor program was discovery of a method for controlling electron flow in a semiconductor so as to achieve amplification without the inherent disadvantages of the vacuum tube. Shockley, on theoretical grounds, had shown that amplification should be possible, but no one knew just how this goal might be achieved. It was decided to direct the program toward increased understanding of the way electric current flows in semiconductors rather than toward the development of an amplifier.

I joined the group late in 1945 to work on solid-state theory without having chosen an area of study. It was chance rather than design that led me into the semiconductor program. Since the large influx of wartime research personnel had not yet dissipated and the new building program had not yet been completed, the laboratories were relatively crowded. I shared an office with Walter Brattain and Gerald Pearson, both of whom were interested in semiconductors; by process of osmosis, I too became interested.

At the time, the basis for a theory of semiconductors had been proposed, but there was little correspondence between theory and experiment except in a very qualitative way. It was not known whether the theory itself was incomplete or whether the far from ideal materials used in early experiments were responsible for the discrepancies. Prior to the war, most experimental work had been done on copper oxide and selenium because of their commercial importance. During the war, as we have mentioned, much research was done on germanium and silicon. Methods were developed for their preparation in fairly pure form and for control of their electric properties with appropriate doping by impurities. Since these materials appeared to lend themselves more readily to basic understanding, it was decided to concentrate on them.

An outgrowth of the program was the discovery of a new method for changing the conductivity of a semiconductor by current flow from an appropriate contact. This discovery led to the inventions of the point-contact and junction transistors. There followed an intense period of device development and basic semiconductor research. Single crystals of germanium or silicon of very high purity or of carefully controlled composition, produced primarily for device research, proved invaluable for certain basic research studies. As the theory of semiconductors was refined and extended, quantitative correlation between theory and experiment was achieved for many properties, often in intricate detail. For a while, semiconductor research became one of the most popular fields of physics. Physical Society meetings frequently devoted several sessions to the subject. During this period, the bulk of basic research on semiconductors, both theoretical and experimental, was done in industrial laboratories. There was, and still is, a free flow of information among the various laboratories engaged in these investigations.

More recently, interest in the basic physics of semiconductors has tapered off to some extent, but device development goes on apace, with integrated circuits, junction lasers, and a renewed interest in field-effect devices. The principle on which field-effect devices operate was suggested by Shockley prior to the invention of junction transistors, but it required considerable development of semiconductor technology to make them practical. It seems that every year or two a new development comes along, which provides the field with a new impetus. Probably in no other area, incidentally, has there been so close a relationship between basic and applications research: often the same people have been involved in both.

Xerography

Xerography is dependent on electrostatics and photoconductivity in very high electric fields. Electrostatics is one of the oldest branches of physics, but for a long time it was also one of the most neglected. Much research had been done on various aspects of photoconductivity, but little on charge transport in materials and under conditions essential to xerography. Thus the technology was unfamiliar, and even the earliest work — that done at Battelle Memorial Institute — required some fairly basic studies.

A dozen years ago — when I first began to consult with Xerox, then the Haloid Company — the entire research and development xerography program was located in an old converted frame house. The essential goal of the company at that time was the development of salable products to support this research program and resultant practical applications. As sales expanded, more effort was plowed into research. At this stage, however, emphasis had to be placed on applied research; only modest support was available for basic studies. The most outstanding accomplishment of this period was the development of the 914 machine. Not only a great technical achievement, it was perhaps even more an innovation as a product and marketing concept. It represented systems engineering in the best sense. Nevertheless, its development strained technology to its limits and required a large investment in applied research.

With the success of the 914 machine, the interests of the company broadened to encompass a wide segment of the graphic arts, and a much-expanded program of basic research was undertaken. This program, under the direction of W. W. Tyler, is developing rapidly and will constitute an important contribution to the potential of Xerox for future growth. It is supplemented by the continuing work at Battelle Memorial Institute and by the fairly basic studies, largely directed toward military and space programs, of an excellent group of scientists in the laboratories of Electro-Optical Systems — now a subsidiary of Xerox. In short, a broad research base exists for company expansion.

Superconductivity

Scientists from all over the world have contributed importantly to our knowledge of superconductivity, the field in which my own research activities have been largely centered for the past several years. In part because a theory is now available on the basis of which experimentation can be suggested or interpreted, and in part because superconductors have been discovered that withstand high magnetic fields, this area has undergone recent phenomenal growth. Although the main interest in the remarkable properties of superconductors is purely scientific, there are now applications, the most important of which is the superconducting magnet, made possible by the discovery of superconductors that withstand very high magnetic fields. This discovery was an outgrowth of a research program on superconducting alloys and compounds, initiated by B. Matthias and J K. Hulm primarily to further scientific understanding of superconductivity.

Differences in Interaction

These three areas — semiconductor electronics, xerography, and superconductivity — illustrate different ways in which basic research can interact with technology. The Bell Telephone Laboratories chose to study semiconductors because of their potential importance for advancing the art of electric communications; initial research was basic in nature, but investigators were well aware of long-range practical goals. Xerography came into being through an ingenious invention, but a new technology had to be developed for its exploitation. Pure scientific interest in a mysterious and remarkable phenomenon motivates most research on superconductivity; at the same time, attempts to exploit the very unusual properties observed are gradually leading to applications.

TRAINING FOR TECHNOLOGY

It was at a conference on superconductivity, held at the new IBM laboratory at Yorktown Heights in 1961, that Brian Pippard gave his well-known and controversial talk entitled "The Cat and the Cream." [2] He pictured industrial laboratories as the cat and interesting scientific problems in solid-state and low-temperature physics as the cream, expressing concern over the rapid pace of scientific progress in such areas of interest to industry. His fear was that all the really interesting and challenging scientific problems would be so quickly solved that within ten years a "scientific dust bowl" might well exist in these fields. He also went on to discuss the difficulties faced by the person in academic life, whose responsibility it is to select challenging problems for a constant flow of graduate students — problems on which students can successfully work at their own pace in competition with full-time professionals in industrial laboratories. He acknowledged the continuing need for technology but wondered how to get first-class people interested in it and how to train them properly.

It seems to me that Pippard was being overly pessimistic. It was not long after his talk that one of his own students, Brian Josephson, suggested a tunneling phenomenon in superconductors that opened up new areas of experimentation which have already led to a deeper understanding of superconductivity. As the frontiers of knowledge are pushed back, the periphery expands and new problems arise. Nevertheless, though Pippard may have overstated his case, the problems he posed are real ones. How should one train students for development and engineering work in new fields such as semiconductor electronics and superconductivity that require a knowledge of advanced concepts of modern physics? A great deal of soul-searching is currently going on in our graduate schools of engineering in an attempt to find answers to this question.

It is pertinent to note that basic research programs in industrial laboratories can constitute an important means for introducing first-class people to technology and applied research. Anticipation of continuing the sort of basic research done as a graduate student can be used to attract such people into the industrial research laboratory. There, through contact with those working on applications, many may find an unsuspected challenge in applied research and development problems and may transfer their interests in this direction.

INFORMATION TRANSFER

It is highly appropriate that we conclude this discussion by emphasizing the vital need for improved channels of scientific

communication. Prompt and efficient information transfer between laboratories engaged in research in any rapidly developing
field of science, nationally and internationally, is essential. It is
made difficult by the pace of modern progress and by the numbers
of people involved. Scientific publications and meetings, personal
contacts, and occasional personnel exchanges between research
institutions meet only a part of this need. Industrial organizations
can maintain a degree of contact with university research through
academic consultants. Libraries and specialized information services have a useful role to play. But these avenues, singly or collectively, are inadequate. New concepts must be explored, communications must be improved, in order that basic research
programs may be made more effective for all concerned.

It is not impossible that Xerox will repay in part its debt to
science by speeding information exchange through advances in
the field of graphic communications.

[1] The Symposium on Basic Research, sponsored by the National Academy of Sciences
and other agencies in 1959, contains an excellent discussion of basic research problems:
see AAAS Publication No. 56 (1959).

[2] Brian Pippard, "The Cat and the Cream," *Physics Today*, **14** (No. 11), 38 (1961).

Innovation and
Experimentation in Education

Jerome B. Wiesner
Dean, School of Science, Massachusetts Institute of Technology

Two ingredients are recognized by most of industry as essential to growth and progress: research, to provide an ever-better understanding of the basic sciences that underly a company's products; and development, to continuously improve old products and create new ones through engineering advances. The new Xerox laboratory for research on information processing that has occasioned this dedicatory symposium reflects a recognition of these needs by the hardheaded businessmen who have built the Xerox Corporation to its present greatness.

Similar motivations for research exist in the field of education. Regrettably, they are only partially recognized by people in responsible positions.

Progressive industry expects to invest as much as five per cent of its gross income in its future, and it considers the money well spent. By contrast, the education enterprise in the United States, a thirty-billion-dollar industry, spends only about twenty-five million dollars a year on curriculum development. If we add to this sum the monies spent on designing new desks and chairs and the other fancy paraphernalia advertised by the school supply companies, we swell the total; but I submit that curriculum material is the product most sorely in need of creative effort and development.

The company or entire industry that lacks the vision to invest in its future usually falls by the wayside, or at least fails to keep pace with the economy. If we, as a nation, fail to invest in the future of our educational system, we can expect the same serious consequences on a larger scale. It is our children who suffer when teaching is less than adequate.

CONFERENCE ON MUSIC EDUCATION

I should like to describe for you at some length a conference held at Yale University in 1963 to evaluate American musical education in the primary and secondary schools. This music seminar was one activity among many undertaken by a panel of outstanding educators under the sponsorship of the Federal Government to explore the opportunities for innovation and experiment in education. The panel was sponsored jointly by the U.S. Commissioner of Education, the Director of the National Science Foundation, and the Office of Science and Technology, which I headed as Special Assistant to the President; it was chaired by Dr. J. R. Zacharias of Massachusetts Institute of Technology, the originator and leader of the Physical Sciences Study Group whose work on high school physics has pointed the way for much of the other work done on curriculum reform.

The following are excerpts from the glowing account of the seminar written by Eric Saltzman, composer and music critic for the *New York Times*, in June, 1963:

The conference . . . was a remarkable meeting of representatives of every aspect of American musical life and activity, who came together with the aim of evaluating and re-evaluating American musical education in the primary and secondary schools. . . . Somehow, the congruence of a variety of vastly differing musical backgrounds, minds, points of view, and approaches produced clear outlines of new concepts of music teaching designed to involve children in genuine and profound musical experiences.

The impulse for the seminar came from, of all places, the President's Office of Science and Technology; the event was financed by the United States Office of Education. The prototypes for the meeting can be found in the fields of science and mathematics. The Sputnik Age found American basic scientific education still in the age of Euclid and Newton; distinguished scientists and mathematicians, working through the prestige and good offices of the Government, have brough tabout an educational revolution from the primary grades on up. Now, for the first time, it was being asked whether similar reforms were not needed in one of the arts and the answer was emphatically in the affirmative.

The thirty participants in the seminar included a large group of composer-educators and composer-performers,[1] performers,[2] critics, theoreticians, musicologists, and ethnomusicologists.

There was agreement that American public school music education had its bright spots and positive achievements. The high technical

73

quality of band, orchestra, and choral performance was often cited, and individual examples of excellent educational achievement were brought forward.

The general situation across the country, however, was found to be very poor. In most schools, in the elementary grades, untrained classroom teachers are charged with the responsibility of giving children the basic music skills which the teachers, themselves, do not possess; and the means and equipment provided for the purpose of accomplishing this hopeless goal are almost invariably inadequate and antimusical.

Interestingly enough, there was almost no conflict on these points between the educators and the "practicing" musicians. The educators were convinced of the magnitude of the problem and of the need for close contact [with] the living world of music creation and performance, just as practicing musicians were sensitive to the need for close involvement in the educational process from the lowest grades.

If the twelve days of panels, papers, discussions, section meetings, and plenary sessions produced any ideological divisions at all, it was primarily between those who wanted to place the principal emphasis on the great Western tradition of the last two centuries and the strong group who felt it was at least as important to broaden our musical and education horizons to include early Western music, recent avant-garde developments (including electronic music), as well as nonconcert music of all types.

A great deal of emphasis was put not only on the children's performance activities, but also on creativity; there was wide agreement as to the importance of a program designed to foster creative musical ex-

pression from the earliest grades as a means of building and training basic musicality in every child.

The importance of student involvement and activity at every level of the educational process was a constant theme of the discussions. The experience of live music was also stressed and, in this connection, it was urged that solo performers and chamber music ensembles be brought into the schools on an in-residence basis similar to that already used in the Ford Foundation's composer-in-residence program.

The work of the seminar was only a first step. Its conclusions will be described in a report to the Office of Education. The report will serve both as a mandate and as a guide for the work of a follow-up committee that will have the responsibility of finding ways of implementing these ideas in practical terms.

THE NEW SCIENCE CURRICULA

General Development

The music seminar described above was considered by some a rather extreme departure from the parochial problems of science and technology. In fact, though, it represented a perfectly natural evolution of work begun a decade ago to improve the quality of science teaching in our elementary and secondary schools — an effort that has seen the creation and introduction of new high school curricula in biology, mathematics, physics, and chemistry. In these areas, new courses are already in use; others are being developed from the same mold for the humanities, including art, music, and history. Analogous efforts are in progress at the college level in several fields of science. Also, special similarly designed courses in science and mathematics are being prepared for use in tropical Africa.

Experience to date with the new science courses has demonstrated convincingly that employing scientific methods can be as productive in the development of new teaching materials as in the creation of a new photocopying machine. And, as in an engineering effort, teams of experts working together are required to produce a satisfactory product. Outstanding research scientists and science teachers participated in developing the science courses, but they required the assistance of professionals in such other fields as moviemaking, testing, bookmaking, and equipment design.

The Physical Sciences Study Group Course in Physics

The Physical Sciences Study Group — that which I know best — started work in 1956 and is still developing some of its materials. The group designed a modern physics course and then embodied it in a new textbook, a new set of experiments, new examinations, new laboratory guides, a series of paperback books on related scientific subjects, new teachers' guides, a set of instructional films, films for teacher preparation, laboratory films, and other instructional aids. In accord with the customary industrial development pattern, the new materials were tested in selected schools, evaluated by selected teachers, and ultimately released for general use.

The total effort, supported largely by the National Science Foundation, cost approximately one million dollars a year for five years. This sounds like a great deal of money, particularly if one compares it to the cost of supporting a lone teacher on a part-time basis to write a textbook in his spare time. When one considers, however, that American schools spend approximately a hundred million dollars a year on the teaching of high school physics, the million-dollars-a-year figure for product development does not seem out of line. Much of the total sum was used to support testing and teacher participation.

By 1964, almost half of the 400,000 students enrolled in physics courses in United States high schools were taking the new Physical Sciences Study Group course. Twenty-four per cent of the nation's 16,500 physics teachers had by then been trained to teach it. Also noteworthy is the fact that the materials have been translated into many foreign languages and are in current use overseas.

SUPPORT: EDUCATIONAL RESEARCH AND DEVELOPMENT

The idea that education development is a good investment enjoys widespread acceptance. Unfortunately, however, when a choice must be made between this long-range effort and immediate operational costs, the pressing short-term needs receive most of the available funds. This may sound like the complaint of a typical research enthusiast who feels that his work is *never* properly supported. It is no such thing. I am simply airing some long-standing frustrations acquired during my tour of duty in Washington.

I tried very hard to persuade the management of the National Science Foundation to assign a high priority to educational research and development, but with little success. In 1961, the total NSF budget for curriculum development was seven million dollars, and there were few other funds available for this type of activity. A review of actual program opportunities that year indicated a need for approximately twenty-five million dollars to finance the really promising work then in sight. After some discussion, the director of the Science Foundation was encouraged to request twenty million dollars for support of this work during the following budget year. But when Congress approved an over-all NSF budget smaller than had been submitted, only about nine million dollars was allocated for curriculum research and development. Considerably larger sums were allocated for and spent on teacher-training institutes, laboratory equipment for secondary schools and colleges, and other facilities dedicated to the short-term improvement of science teaching.

Why the imbalance in favor of the short-term view? Investigation revealed that other program directors — those responsible for basic scientific research activities, teacher-training programs, and science equipment programs — could demonstrate immediate and pressing needs. Without additional funds, students would not have the laboratory facilities they needed. Summer training institutes would not be able to accommodate all the teachers who wished to attend. Congressmen would be besieged with complaints if teacher salaries were not increased. In the face of such heavy demands, the arguments for a major share of the new money were very forceful — and very successful.

I do not wish to leave the impression that I am opposed to such expenditures. I believe, in fact, that they could profitably be increased. What I do object to is the lack of a reasonable balance.

There is a special irony in this situation. Whenever budgets get tight, basic research funds are the first to be cut. And within the basic research category, the National Science Foundation is usually hit first and most severely. The reason is a simple one: the agency has no applied missions and consequently no development funds behind which to hide research support when basic research is unpopular. The Defense Department succeeded in supporting a healthy and growing research and development effort during the Eisenhower economy years, even in the face of Secretary Wilson's publicly avowed disdain for research. Is it not incongruous that the Science Foundation — so often the first victim of budget restrictions — should, under the above circumstances, have failed to appreciate the importance of adequate support for the developments that would have made their large, continuing investments in education more effective?

Dr. Leland Haworth, the new director of the National Science Foundation, strongly favors basic work, and there is hope that the future will bring to it the kind of emphasis its potential justifies. But it will not be a victory easily won. Only recently, a part of the curriculum program designed to improve mathematics teaching in tropical Africa was held back; the excuse: an emergency need for blackboards and erasers somewhere in the AID program.

PANEL ON EDUCATIONAL RESEARCH AND DEVELOPMENT

The Panel on Educational Research and Development was established to explore the extent to which the opportunities revealed by the science teaching studies might exist in nonscientific areas. In connection with these earlier studies, however, two disclaimers should be stated:

First, people have designed courses before and have attempted to integrate text material, laboratory equipment, and auxiliary teaching aids. Others have built experimental schools and have formulated new programs for teacher education. But the recent efforts in science have been both qualitatively and quantitatively different. They have brought together large concentrations of talent and provided adequate supporting personnel and materials. They have applied the same force and discipline to the creation of a new course that industry would muster to develop a piece of sophisticated apparatus.

Second, though I have referred to research and development, most of the work I have cited has had little true research associated with it. Though it involved experimentation, it concerned itself primarily with engineering development, attempting to use existing tools and existing knowledge in the most effective way. There has been, from the start, a recognition of the need for a better understanding of human learning processes, testing procedures, reading techniques, and many other aspects of the educational process; but curriculum development was not allowed to wait for research in these fields. It is our hope that as educational research and development gains greater appreciation, such fundamental work will become more stylish. Perhaps one day it may even be respectable for outstanding psychologists to study learning processes in children instead of in rats.

Panel Composition

The Panel on Educational Research and Development was made up of professional educators, psychologists, and many scholars in specific fields. The names and affiliations of Panel members are listed at the end of this paper.[3]

Basic Goals

In its first report,[4] dated March, 1964, the Panel described its basic goals as follows:

The general aim of the Panel is to identify research and development programs that might be of major benefit to the wide range of educational activities carried on by various Federal offices and agencies, including the Office of Education and the National Science Foundation.

One aim of the Panel is to attract to the service of education outstanding people outside the educational system. People engaged professionally in activities related to subjects taught in the schools — in scientific research, writing, making music, running a city — have something indispensable to contribute to education, not just as "resource persons" but as participants in the creation and evaluation of instruc-

tional tools and procedures. The schools have been off in a box by them-selves too long.

The task is not only to persuade scholars and practitioners to work on education but also to devise new administrative frameworks, new institutions, by which such people can work with teachers and school principals on a continuing basis. Outstanding scholars have partici-pated in the science and mathematics programs, including such Nobel prize winners as E. M. Purcell, Glenn T. Seaborg, H. J. Muller, and W. M. Stanley. The Panel's experience reveals a comparable willing-ness among workers in other fields.

Methods of Operation

The Panel conducts business, and works to persuade other groups to conduct business, in several ways. There are, first, the regular meetings of the Panel. Guests are frequently invited to these meetings to expand the range of competence in the room and to present special views. Growing out of such Panel discussions are a variety of 1-day and 2-day meetings to develop points of particular interest to the Panel; 5 to 15 people take part in these meetings, a few of them chosen from the Panel but most of them expert in appropriate fields. These meetings have been held on such topics as teacher education and nongraded schools. The meetings develop new ideas but serve mainly as ways to explore the feasibility of making larger studies, and in some cases to develop possible plans of approach for such studies. Finally, there are the larger studies, or seminars, lasting approximately two weeks and con-sisting of 30 to 50 people, again including a few people from the Panel. The seminars have been held on such topics as learning about learning, music education, and education for the deprived and segregated.

The seminars, and the other meetings too, serve as means of attracting new people to educational reform. The reports of the seminars serve both as guidelines for future action and as mandates for that action. Reports include information about what is going on in a given area, what might, ideally, go on in that area, and how to get it done. Reports also include estimates of the size of the job and suggest possible mechanisms — physical arrangements and sources of support — for conducting research and development.

Work in Progress

As one of its first tasks, the Panel drew up a list of areas other than science and mathematics in which research and development seemed needed. The list — contained in the Panel report and repeated here — though formidable, is admittedly incomplete. It includes: *learning about learning, music, teacher education, education of the deprived and segregated, vocational education, reading, arts, graphic art, and skills, English composition, social studies, programmed instruction, audio-visual aids, education of principals, school administration, teachers' pay and prerequisites, education of women, adult and continuing education, libraries, history, educational testing, museums, bricks and mortar.*

A number of these areas have been examined preliminarily in the manner described by the report. In a few areas, work is actively under way, but a very small part of the total task has been completed. All studies to date, including that of teacher education, have been limited to elementary and secondary school needs.

Areas of study have been so selected that several basic investigations can be carried on simultaneously. Learning about learning and learning about reading are both essential to long-range progress. Music education affords an opportunity to explore the possibilities of experimentation and innovation in a field very different from science. Teacher education is at the heart of any effort to improve education. Education for the deprived and segregated deals with one of the most serious challenges faced today by our nation and by its educational system in particular.

Some Early Results

Detailed results on each of the studies mentioned in the paragraph above appear in the previously cited Panel report.[4] Since specifics best convey the excitement and opportunity that characterize the work of the Panel, permit me to abstract a few of the highlights for you.

Music Education. As Mr. Saltzman's report indicated, a number of ideas for improving music education were explored during the 1963 music seminar, and many of them are being studied in current experimental programs. At the Juilliard School of Music, for example, an attempt is being made to develop a music series that will begin in the elementary school and continue through high school.

The seminar set as one goal the production of a really new and really musical music curriculum for the schools. Ideally, the repertory would be designed to develop musical taste, not to cater to it. The students would be guided to approach music, within the limits of their abilities, in the same way that musicians do. The repertory would include many different kinds of music. The basic materials would be musical parts and scores and books of song from which the youngsters would sing and perform. Hopefully, a variety of supporting materials would be developed, as in the science programs: teachers' guides, as well as records, films, and supplements on music qualities and history. The new materials would be tested extensively in the schools to permit revision and thorough development prior to general distribution.

Also suggested during the seminar was the use of the inductive method for the teaching of music. The repertory would form the basis for teaching musical, general harmonic, and tonal structure, music history, and music literature — all inductively. Musical principles would be drawn from the music the children themselves performed. Formal instruction would be given at a more advanced level.

A third idea developed at the seminar was that, from kindergarten on, children should be taught not simply to perform and listen to other people's music but to improvise and to write music themselves. Here again there might be a natural sequence of development: improvisation, then invention of music without writing it down, then composition in written notation — all coupled with rehearsing and performing the student's own work. It is probable that, given the opportunity, many children would demonstrate originality and creativity in musical composition. Very few today have a sufficient knowledge or opportunity to do so.

Finally, the seminar urged that professional musicians be brought into the schools. A variety of activities come to mind that would excite and stimulate the musical interests of students, whether through string quartets, woodwind ensembles, jazz combos, or other such groups. The arrangement could work to the mutual advantage of musicians and schools: it would be good for education and it would be good for music.

These are but a few of the music teaching possibilities exposed by the seminar. Many would seem to be obvious, yet it will take a great deal of effort to ready them for introduction into the schools in really usable form.

Learning about Learning. One fact has impressed me more than any other as I have become increasingly involved with the teaching industry: few good scientists have been attracted to work on the fundamental aspects of learning — or on the educational process altogether, for that matter. The generally hopeful conclusions of the Conference on Learning held at Cambridge during June, 1962, under the leadership of Dr. Jerome S. Bruner, brighten prospects for the future in this area. The conference produced a long and detailed report — about to be published as a monograph by the U.S. Office of Education — which sets forth guidelines for a number of specific psychological and educational research activities centered around the theory of instruction. It suggests a critical examination of programmed learning; investigation into the use of computers for instructional purposes; a study of the relationship between testing and learning; studies concerning the best relationships between the learner and a tutor. Several research projects have already resulted from the conference and subsequent meetings. It is my hope that this is only a start, and that with passing time we will be able to establish really sound patterns of instruction based upon deep understanding.

Improving Teacher Quality. All members of the Panel agreed on the two prerequisites most essential to an improved educational system: improved teacher preparation and attraction of more able youngsters into the teaching profession. Particular emphasis was placed on the fact that teachers, on the whole, need to be better prepared in the substance of the subjects they teach. This does not necessarily mean that they must have an advanced and sophisticated knowledge of these subjects, but they should be well versed in the basic materials.

One of the most important aspects of the science curriculum development programs is the great stress placed upon teacher training. Special training guides are produced and distributed, films are created especially for teachers, special institutes are held, and a continual effort is made to communicate with those teachers who are using the new materials.

Most institutions offering instruction in pedagogy, in the opinion of the Panel, not only provide an inadequate background in the subject matter for which they are training teachers, but also take too abstract and general an approach to the problems of teaching. A major effort is needed to make this important element of our educational system more effective. In this connection, the Panel further observed:

. . . in improving the education of teachers, the problem is not only

to develop new modes of education but also to develop rapid ways to disseminate new ideas. Indeed, in view of the numbers of people involved (there are approximately 1.8 million teachers in our primary and secondary schools), devising an efficient way to disseminate ideas becomes a major aspect of the problem.

Efforts at improvement must affect education at three levels, each well-populated: (1) the pre-service education of new teachers, where new programs might be fitted into the existing educational scheme; (2) the in-service education of teachers, which may require the development of new kinds of programs and institutions; and (3) the education of the teachers of the teachers, a group that would include both professors and master teachers involved in practice-teaching programs.

A particularly effective method of training teachers is to involve them in curriculum development activities. This approach was inadvertently developed during the course of the work on the new science programs. Since it was considered necessary to have the advice and guidance of teachers actually working continually with the students in the high schools, a large number of high school teachers became involved. They made major contributions to the work, and at the same time became thoroughly familiar with the new material. Such participation could be made an essential part of a teacher's education, requiring that he assist with the development or testing of a new course or do work on some other aspect of education research. Activities of this type might even be incorporated into a doctoral program, possibly in a graduate school of education.

Another important aspect of this intellectual activity is the upgrading of the image of education and of teachers that it helps to bring about. When it is possible to attract some of the country's best minds to elementary and secondary education, as we have been able to do during the past several years, there inevitably develops a somewhat greater public respect for this activity. If educational innovation, experimentation, and research become generally accepted as a continuing part of the ongoing educational process — just as they are recognized as essential activities within the Xerox Corporation — large numbers of students and teachers will have an opportunity to participate in the work. I expect that many more of our best young people will then be attracted to the teaching profession, with a consequent improvement of quality all along the line. For several years there has been a steady decline in the number of the most able students who choose education as their life's work. I believe that challenging research activity of the type I have been discussing could reverse this trend.

One final point should be emphasized while I am talking about teachers. With good curriculum material, properly planned, it becomes possible to take the teacher out of the circuit, so that the inadequately trained teacher does not set the ceiling for the student. There will probably never be a substitute for the stimulation provided by an inspired teacher. But the simple fact is that a very large percentage of teachers in the elementary and secondary schools have never had the opportunity to become adequately trained. This is particularly true in the sciences. Here the problem can be met in two ways. First, by means of the various teacher-training materials — films, texts, institutes, and the like — we can provide the wherewithal for the teacher to help himself. Second, it is possible to plan courses in such a way that the bright student, with just a bit of initiative, can progress beyond the teacher if he wants to. Inexpensive laboratory kits and movies to explain the difficult parts of experiments can allow a student to develop on his own. Outstanding scientists, like Purcell, Seaborg, and Zacharias, can — again by means of film — carry scientific discussions to higher levels and at the same time provide for the student an impression of the kind of people scientists are and how they work and think. Inexpensive paperback books, like the dozens prepared for the physics course, can provide a rich and varied field for exploration beyond the range of the basic text and the scope of the classroom teacher. The opportunities here are endless.

Incidentally, I am convinced that similar activities would pay off handsomely in the developing nations, where the problem of providing an adequate supply of competent teachers is very much worse than it is in the United States.

I have touched very briefly on a number of subjects that deserve fuller treatment. My purpose has been to provide only a glimpse of the variety of possibilities that exist for the application of experimentation to the improvement of the educational process. I have omitted more topics than I have included, and I very much regret some of the omissions. I am certain that you would share my enthusiasm over the studies now in progress on education for the deprived and segregated in this country and over the African mathematics and science studies to which I have alluded.

Progress in these areas holds forth the hope that a circle of desperation can be broken: a circle enforced by the lack of educational opportunity and re-enforced by lack of background, motivation, and facilities; a circle that, unless broken, completely condemns succeeding generations.

The task of education, both at home and abroad, seems so unending that people despair of beginning. But we have begun; and if the work is backed by the American people with the same kind of dedication that was given to the space effort, we can transform our entire academic system. Transform it we must, for it is no longer adequate to the demands made upon it by the society into which its students graduate.

[1] Lukas Foss, Leon Kirschner, Edward J. Cone, Otto Luening, Henry Brant, Lionel Nowak, Howard Boatwright, Gid Waldrop; and from the jazz field, Billy Taylor and Mercer Ellington.

[2] Adele Addison, Noah Greenberg, Milton Katims.

[3] Members of the Panel on Educational Research and Development: Jerrold R. Zacharias (Chairman), Professor of Physics, M.I.T.; James E. Allen, Jr., Commissioner of Education, New York State; B. Frank Brown, Principal, Melbourne High School, Melbourne, Florida; Jerome S. Bruner, Center for Cognitive Studies, Harvard University; Frederick Burkhardt, President, American Council of Learned Societies; Bowen C. Dees, Associate Director, National Science Foundation; Charles A. Ferguson, Director, Center for Applied Linguistics; John H. Fischer, President, Teachers' College, Columbia University; Ralph C. M. Flynt, Associate Commissioner for Educational Research and Development, U.S. Office of Education; Sister M. Jacqueline Grennan, S.L., Vice-President, Webster College; Martin Mayer; Sterling M. McMurrin, Department of Philosophy, University of Utah; S. M. Nabrit, President, Texas Southern University; Marcus G.

Raskin, Co-Director, Institute for Policy Studies; Patrick Suppes, Institute for Mathematical Studies in the Social Sciences, Stanford University; Ralph W. Tyler, Director, Center for Advanced Study in the Behavioral Sciences; Benjamin C. Willis, General Superintendent of Schools, Chicago, Illinois.

[4] "Innovation and Experiment in Education: A Progress Report of the Panel on Educational Research and Development to the U.S. Commissioner of Education, the Director of the National Science Foundation, and the Special Assistant to the President for Science and Technology," United States Government Printing Office, Washington, D.C., March, 1964.

Communications Science —
Today and Tomorrow

W. O. Baker

Vice-President, Research, Bell Telephone Laboratories

The United States of America has, since its founding, kept a great idea. It is that independent, private enterprises can discover and provide for the well-being and security of all the people certain common services like transportation, much higher education, medical care, and communications. This remains one of the daringly successful concepts of history. Truly, here the responsibility of the citizens, given such chances to serve, complements that of democratic governments and far transcends that of the components in collectivist societies. But a query constantly to be made is: How are we doing? Especially in an Age of Science, is this bold scheme of free endeavor really competitive in scope and quality with what monolithic authorities can do? This notable occasion, the dedication of a new Xerox laboratory, in effect celebrates the vitality of invention and of industrial growth under our system, and offers a good opportunity to report on one fraction of this situation — how the science and technology of communications seem to be shaping up to meet the needs of society in the busy years to come.

In this symposium on the impact of science and technology on society, we think of communications and their future as involving every aspect of the transfer of information within and among organisms. Clearly, we shall be able to reflect on only a tiny sample of the scientific and technical features of communication. Thus, it is seemly to seek some feature of the technical aspects of communications which especially fits this distinguished festivity. Such a one may be a feature which is not irrelevant to the time and place in which we are. This is the feature of replication or repetition, often periodicity in time and space, of events and/or structures. Replication is, of course, an information-passing or communication process fundamental to order — to the ordering of the universe, in some respects to order in the structure of atoms and molecules (especially within polymer molecules), to the structure of solid matter, and above all, to the structure of organisms and living systems.

It also appears that replication of events stands out in the evolution of conventional human communications, since our ability to articulate language reproducibly, to write (even if not legibly!), and to recognize written patterns repetitively, is the basis for most information transfer. When civilization had advanced to the point at which languages and writing and speech were pretty well developed, people recognized the ability to encode these signals by rather elementary events, particularly on-and-off, yes-or-no, plus-or-minus kinds of events. These smoke signals, or telegraphs,

94

or whatever, were very slow and usually expressionless. But it was long after Morse code, and following the early considerations of Nyquist, Hartley, and others, who were themselves stimulated by the demonstrations that human communications could be transmitted electrically, in either coded or electrical analog form, that Shannon discovered information theory. Shannon showed that binary events, so long as they were enacted often enough (namely, about twice as often in time as the period fluctuations, or frequency, necessary to represent the basic event of speech, vision, number tables, etc.), could express accurately the whole information content involved. He revealed also that the entropy of language, pictures, and other information forms permitted a high efficiency of coding and use of bandwidth. The information content of an event is proportional to the inverse natural logarithm of its probability. Fig. 1 illustrates this concept for letters of the alphabet.

Having reached this stage of understanding after millennia in man's history, we see that the process of replication of simple events — pulses of positive or negative electricity, the pointing north or south of tiny magnetic domains, placement of atoms or even electric charges in a certain way in a crystal lattice, the sequence of amino acid residues aggregating beside a desoxyribonucleic acid helix chain — can communicate essentially the whole gamut of human experience and of information.

The recognition of this simple concept, that replication of virtually any form of knowledge, of communication, of signaling, can effectively be achieved by combinations of simple binary

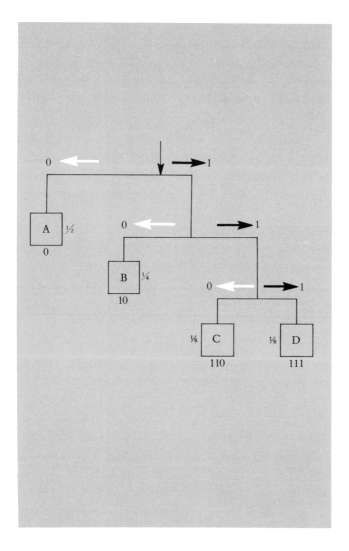

Fig. 1.
Diagram of the binary coding process,
according to Shannon's ideas, is shown
for English letters, taking account of the
probability of their occurrence in language.
Thus, the usage of letter A in English is
considered to be so much more probable
than the letter D that it is given a weight
of ½ in comparison to a weight of ⅛ for
the letter D.

processes, has the profoundest meaning for the future. For I believe that it means that we do not face severe blocks in the continued harmonizing of man's confused life with nature's serene and splendid ways. It appears that we shall be able to deal in some way with the apparent infinities of ordering systems for society, of linking the billions of men on earth with their fellow billions, above all of accumulating, organizing, and preserving man's hard-won knowledge of himself and his world. We shall be able to do so because we are learning to control the replication of structures and of events, which are the essential processes of communication. This may be done within such dimensions and with such economy that we may imagine for society on this planet (and perhaps on others) a macroscopic "nervous system" that functions at least in crude comparison to the elegant self-regulating controls within organisms.

Let us examine the scope of this handling of information for civilization. The subject has been widely surveyed by Professor Fritz Machlup, of Princeton, in his recent book *The Production and Distribution of Knowledge in the United States*. He concludes that this activity, of which communications is the vital flux, is, as a current article in *Fortune* calls it, "The Biggest Growth Industry of Them All," accounting now for about $195 billion of our gross national product, and employment of 24 million persons, some third of all non-farm workers. As to growth, there has been about a 43 per cent expansion in the last five years. E. F. Dennison, in a report to the Committee for Economic Development, asserts that between 1929 and 1957, our rise in real income is 40 per cent from knowledge gain (21 per cent from education of the labor force; 19 per cent from research and development), compared to 14 per cent from capital investment (plant and equipment).

Operations comprising the knowledge industry are given in the following table:

Area of operations	Growth since 1930	Current segment of the industry
Research and development	15-fold	10%
Publishing and printing	10-fold	12%
Entertainment (broadcasting, movies (including sound movies from telephone laboratories), plays, concerts, phonographs (including stereo), records, spectator sports)	2.4-fold	6%
Information machines (typewriters, copying systems, computers, etc.)	14-fold	8%
Professional services (accounting, architecture, medicine, legal information, for businesses)	3-fold	9%
Communications (as knowledge purveyor)	3-fold	7%
Education	4-fold	45%

Dean Wiesner has discussed the education industry. Communication science and technology are just beginning major penetrations of education, with visual and audio aids, TV, programmed instruction, and computer presentation of subject matter. Public schooling costs have gone from $2.6 billion in 1930 to $22 billion in 1963, almost 4-fold per citizen, and higher education costs rose from $632 million to $8.9 billion in the period. The education industry cost of $31 billion is considered by Machlup to be a conservative figure; for all educational activities including instruction in industry, churches, military services, libraries, etc., he derives a total of $60 billion in 1958, or about $86 billion in 1964 (43 per cent increase in five years). Hence as we talk about the future impact of communications technology on society, we could even limit our field to education, and not be talking small. But, of course, we cannot so limit it when other knowledge appetites are recognized in Machlup's terms. Books published in the U.S. held nearly constant in numbers from 1920 to 1954, but have risen 90 per cent since 1958, with about 3 times the dollar sales ($2.4 billion) last year as in 1954. And so it goes, with communications electronics techniques not only influencing printing and distribution, but entering fields like music reproduction (stereo, tapes, hi-fi), architectural acoustics which heighten musical perception, and video in its diverse forms.

Communications services themselves — which have a far narrower area of impact than communications technology — represented a $14.6-billion contribution to the economy in 1963, just for knowledge transmission and switching. Information machines contributed another $11 billion worth, and computers, with hardware and software, added nearly $5 billion more.

But the most interesting aspect of the knowledge industry, accented by Machlup and by Burck in *Fortune,* is its wide-open future. Unlike material consumption — of food, clothing, housing, even, perhaps, of automobiles — there is probably no limit to human needs for knowledge. And many millions of jobs are created in meeting these needs — perhaps 20 million more in the next 20 years. In speaking of an impact of technology on society, we think now of an economic force from a knowledge industry which itself also expresses the highest spiritual and intellectual aspirations of man. We have praised science and engineering as great liberators from physical duress — hunger, cold, disease, drudgery, exhaustion. Much of the world still needs this liberation desperately. But we must also be moving onward to the next stages of man's growth — of mind and spirit, of personal understanding and fulfillment. How happy is the prospect that in this truly endless quest, often a lonely one, the techniques of communications will not only bring man and nations together, but the operations of knowledge-seeking and giving and getting and passing on may gainfully occupy so many of our fellow men. And technological unemployment will long be rare in this field, for the market does expand forever. As Tennyson said:

> Yet all experience is an arch wherethrough
> Gleams that untravelled world, whose margin fades
> Forever and forever when I move.

This is a bold and brave assertion and I shall be able to sustain it only by suggestive examples as we go along. Already, however, you know some of the achievements, which give us great hope for many more. Recent ones include the emergence of solid-state science and engineering, especially in electronics, along with the conception and systems evolution of high-speed logic and memory machines. The modern digital computer has been made functional and efficient by solid-state science embodied in junction diodes, transistors, magnetic memories, integrated circuits; superconducting and optical logic elements are impending. Devices of these types are shown in Figures 2 and 3.

Correspondingly, you also know examples which have facilitated the transmission of information, such as the spanning of space and time by submarine cables and microwave networks and satellite linkages. These also give great hopes, and satellite links powered by shining sheaths of solar cells display again the ceaseless thrust of new discovery going from physics, chemistry, and metallurgy into new engineering modes and actions. Figure 4 shows the Telstar satellite.

But what are the forthcoming thrusts? Doubtless new findings will continue to speed transmission of information, and even more perhaps its switching, among the ever-expanding multitudes of combinations which we wish to be connected to each other. Also, as you know, the discovery of coherent light by Townes, Schawlow, Maiman, Javan, and their associates in *industrial* laboratories (and only secondarily by others, whatever claims international politics and compulsions may have made on this history) has multiplied again our capacity for volume and speed of signals and probably for processing data. Figure 5 shows Javan's lasers.

Now this technique involves, of course, the control of replication of beams of light. Here we could expect great trouble with

Fig. 2.
The modern silicon diode depicted above, compared to an ordinary paper clip in size, has attained a special significance as the radiation counting elements in the Telstar and other satellites and space vehicles. Its capabilities for detecting low-energy electrons and protons are so effective that new maps of the space radiation environment of the earth have been prepared, based on the use of these detectors by W. L. Brown and his associates.

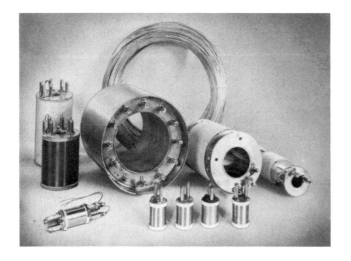

Fig. 3.
Progress in the utilization of superconductivity in metals and alloys is symbolized by the high-field superconductors arising from the work of Kunzler and Matthias. The coils shown are made of Nb_3Sn, which remain superconducting in magnetic fields of greater than 100,000 gauss. Vast new device applications are opened up by this development, which now extends to numerous other compounds and alloys.

Fig. 4.
The Telstar satellite, conceived, designed, and created in the communications industry, was the forerunner of systems of communications satellites now under development by a government corporation and also by military agencies.

Fig. 5.
The glowing tubes of excited gases appearing above are actually emitting coherent light from their ends. They are continuous-wave gas lasers discovered by Javan at the Bell Telephone Laboratories. The light they create is of unprecedented purity and intensity.

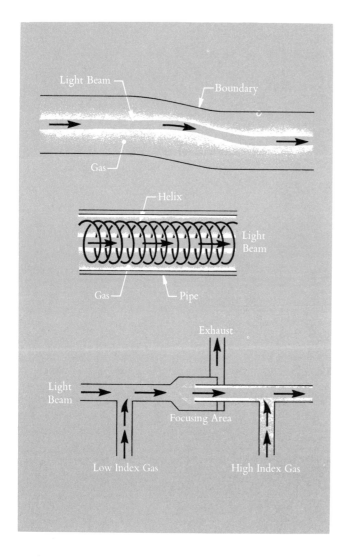

Fig. 6.
The schematic shows a gas lens made by the refraction gradients caused by a thermal (and hence density) variation across a tube containing a gas or, in some cases, a mixture of gases. A narrow, precisely collimated beam of light can be sent long distances with trivial aberration or loss of intensity by this method, discovered by Berreman and Hutson. The diagrams at the bottom of the figure show the way the temperature gradient is produced by a heating helix, on the left, or the way the gradient in composition and hence refractive index is produced by mixing gases, on the right.

lenses which would govern the control and replication of beams over great distances and which have represented a most delicate technical ingredient of science and engineering since the time of Galileo. But Berreman and Hutson have recently invented lenses made of gas — gas whose refractive index or light-bending is made to vary axially as the gas is held in, or runs through, a tube. This is done by heating the gas nonuniformly or mixing different gases so that concentration gradients occur in the tube. Beautiful aberration-free lenses have been obtained (see Figure 6).

Likewise, many other advances in the replication of signals and substances which embody communications are in progress. For instance, while we know that atoms and molecules replicate elegantly the spatial geometry and other qualities of a crystal lattice in growing from a nucleus, it is also technically valuable to have a crystal plane of one kind of atom able to produce a superimposed plane of another kind of atom or mixture of atoms (Figures 7, 8, and 9). This epitaxial growth has been known for a long time in crystallography, and is somewhat related to rain-making by condensation on crystal nuclei. A few years ago, Theurer and co-workers showed it to be an excellent way to make semiconductor devices in which junctions of slightly varying compositions of matter are of great importance. We are beginning to see that this kind of growth can be applied in many new ways indeed.

In replicating the spatial arrangements but not necessarily the composition of many solid systems of atoms and molecules, the exact process of replication of the lattice can be watched by the new technique of low-energy electron diffraction achieved by

Germer and Lander (and also by Farnsworth) (Figure 8). This is now used to show such effects as that of a few layers of aluminum forming over a silicon crystal in exactly the silicon array (Figures 10 and 11). It can even show that the surface atoms of the silicon itself are not bonded together as are those inside the crystal and thus do not have the same geometry or, indeed, electrical and other physical qualities.

These matters of exact crystal replication and periodicity have been also aptly interpreted theoretically in such things as Bardeen's original concept of surface states in semiconductors, notions intimately involved in the discovery of the transistor, and also in the growing understanding we have of the bizarre loss of electrical resistance at the superconducting transition of many metals and alloys. Again, precise and exquisite replication of structure and of composition permit, as conceived by the Bardeen-Cooper-Schrieffer theory, changing interactions of the electrons and lattice. Indeed, Matthias and his co-workers have revealed a whole universe of superconductors, including those which function in magnetic fields of at least 120 kilogauss (see Figures 12 and 13).

But what of the assemblages at surfaces and within molecules that involve more sophisticated communications than those involving the bistate conditions of electrically positive-or-negative conformation, magnetically north-or-south configurations in crystals? We have already said that the latter configurations, thanks to the concepts of information theory and of binary coding, would allow the replication and handling of a great part of the world's knowledge, but how about the modes of communication

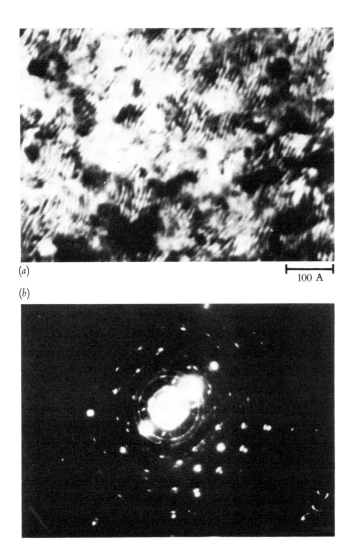

(a)

(b)

100 A

Fig. 7.
*Here (a) is depicted the growth of layers
of germanium atoms on the silicon (110)
planes. According to this work of
Heidenreich and Haase, the moiré patterns
from electron microscope beams
demonstrate the rotational and parallel
displacement of the added planes of
germanium atoms as they seek to adjust to
and replicate the surface of the silicon
crystal. The accompanying illustration (b),
showing the electron diffraction of the thin
surface layer by transmission after the
layer has been isolated electrolytically,
confirms the nearly, but not quite,
successful adjustments of the depositing
germanium to the regular surface it is
attempting to replicate. This is the essence
of the important technological process of
epitaxial preparation of semiconductor
junction devices.*

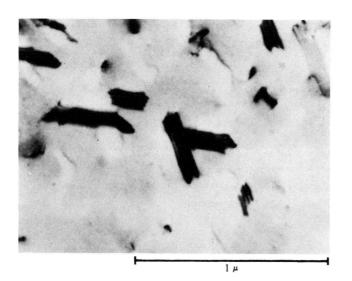

1 μ

Fig. 8.
Here the elegant electron microscopic methods of Heidenreich and Haase reveal the phenomenon of a single crystal surface trying to replicate itself. Silicon is being deposited on the silicon (111) plane. The systems of parallel lines are extinction contours resulting from thickness changes where stacking faults have come into the (111) planes. Probably these faults were begun by scattered oxygen impurity centers on the original, very pure silicon substrate. The features which are not systems of parallel lines represent dislocations in (111) and (110) planes of the silicon.

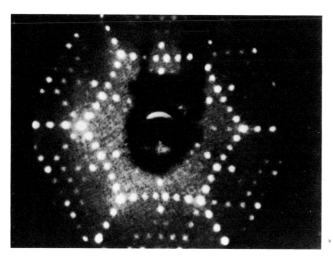

Fig. 9.
The new technique of low-energy electron diffraction yields even more detailed evidence of how the atoms lie at crystal surfaces. The diagram shows the diffraction pattern of a very clean silicon (111) surface. The adjustment of the atoms on this surface to the bonding conditions, which of course are asymmetrical compared to atoms in the bulk of the crystal, causes all but the six brightest hexagonal features to appear.

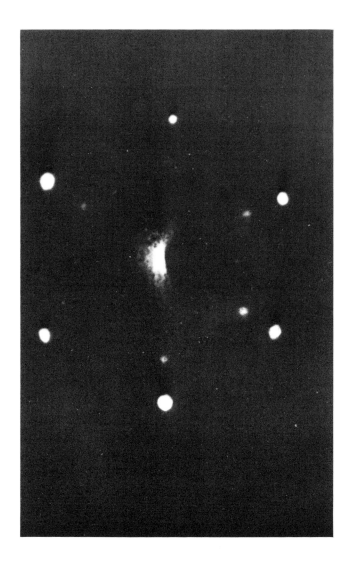

Fig. 10.
Above are the results of the deposition of
about five monolayers of aluminum atoms
evaporated onto the same silicon surface
as was depicted in Fig. 9. In this case, the
low-energy electrons are now scattered
almost exclusively into the six bright,
hexagonally disposed diffraction spots.
These demonstrate a nearly atomically
precise replication of the silicon crystal
substrate.

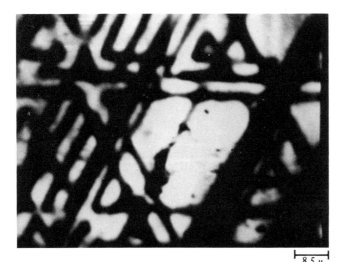

8.5 μ

5 μ

Fig. 11.
A new method of searching for perfection of replication within periodic crystal structures is provided by the work of J. J. Lander and his associates using a fine electron beam microprobe analyzer. The beam is strongly affected by the presence of space charge layers inside semiconductor crystals. For instance, in the upper figure, and also at higher resolution in the lower one, are seen a pattern of slip planes resulting from boron diffusion into the (111) surface of a single crystal of silicon to a depth of about four microns. Thus is displayed with high sensitivity the extraordinary crystal perturbations, even at depths of a few thousand atomic diameters, caused by atoms of slightly differing size and bonding properties to those of the host lattice. The remarkable effect so graphically displayed by the slip plane diagram is the perturbation of large volumes of the basic crystal structure.

Fig. 12.
Pfann, Wagner, and their associates have created a new method of crystal growth which shows a high control of three-dimensional replication. This is called the vapor-liquid-solid process or VLS. An alloy droplet is made supersaturated by receiving additions of its major component from the vapor phase. Thus, we see on the growing silicon crystal a drop of fluid which is actually a good alloy of silicon constantly being supersaturated with additional silicon vapor. The droplet then precipitates out silicon on the growing crystallite.

0.5 mm

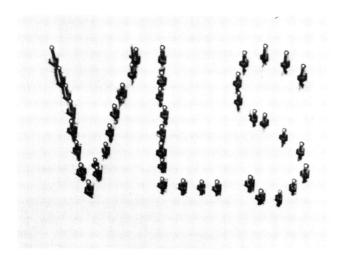

Fig. 13.
The remarkable control of the spatial process shown in Fig. 12 is further illustrated by this figure, depicting the production of a series of precisely replicated single crystal spikes of silicon tracing out the letters VLS as they grow out of a silicon crystal substrate. The extraordinary uniformity in dimensions of these single crystals which have been grown at high temperatures is one of the most remarkable examples of morphological control yet encountered in an inorganic system.

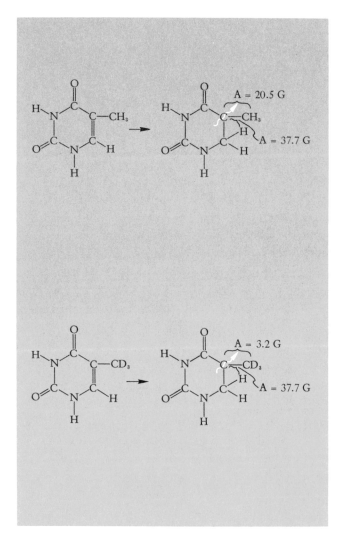

Fig. 14.
The effect of radiation, ranging from nuclear particle bombardment to ultraviolet activation, on the thymine molecule residue is shown here. This constituent base of DNA is converted to radical form at a particular carbon atom by such irradiation. Study of the deuterated methyl group has confirmed the conclusions of Shulman and associates about the position and nature of the radical formation.

involving more animated structures? Still on a molecular scale, we believe that communication of the information for the most vital replication, that of organic structures, occurs through the genes acting through desoxyribonucleic acids to encode the information to be passed on. A copy of this code or, as one could say in terms of self-reproducing machines, a copier of the drawings, is the enzyme DNA polymerase, which will complete replication of a strand of DNA. Then there is the replicating action itself, which is a system of messenger ribonucleic acid, of ribosomes, and of enzymes which will put together amino acids according to the direction of the DNA and, thus, leads to the proteins and other ingredients of the new cell. Great work is going on in revealing the details of this process, which is at the heart of life itself and which is, indeed, the quintessence of replication. But there is space to cite just one example of how expertly this process is being studied in the context of the towering accumulation of modern scientific learning. It is believed that exact replicas embodying the genes are necessary for the propagation of the species, but that rare errors or changes can cause mutations. These, in turn, may even have led to the evolution of species, even to *Homo sapiens*. Perhaps many of these mutations are induced by cosmic rays, a relative of the radiation which in larger quantities terrifies us for the genetic consequences of atomic wars. But we can ask: How precisely does damage from radiation show up in the molecules, in affecting the replicating mechanisms of the genes? And how does Nature try to correct errors in the coding caused thereby?

Lately, Shulman and his associates have shown that a particular sensitivity to radiation occurs in one special group of the complex DNA chain. This response is to form a free radical or unbound place in a part called the thymine residue (Figure 14). It is very interesting, although perhaps just coincidental, that biologists, particularly Drs. Boyce and Flanders of the Yale University Medical School, Dr. Wacker of Germany, and Drs. Setlow and Carrier of the Oak Ridge National Laboratory have been finding that this thymine is also connected with the error-correcting capabilities of genetic codes, and that it functions this way by forming a dimer, or linkage of two adjacent thymines. Anyway, Shulman also finds that these changes caused by radiation, whether nuclear radiation or ultraviolet light radiation, are affected by simple metal ions, whose special roles in living matter have long caused keen curiosity. By modern physical studies, Shulman has been able to derive the position of these metal ions along the DNA chains, and has been able to show that in some cases they reduce the radical formation expected from a given amount of radiation of DNA (Figure 15). Here is a case in which the ability to replicate huge molecules precisely, which governs the very form of life and the evolution of man, may in turn be subject to subtle influences of rather localized fields and valences.

But exploration of the ways in which effects both of matter and of waves can be replicated is being extended to even more complex situations. Beyond the reproduction with genes is the operation of the organism itself. Its internal communication facilities are dominated by systems of neurons whereby they are able

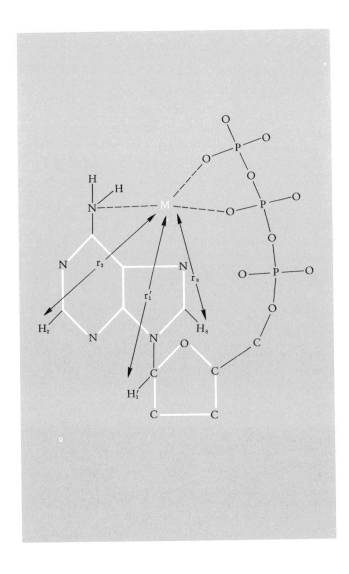

Fig. 15.
This schematic shows the coordination of a typical metal ion, such as Cu^{++}, Co^{++}, and so forth, with the elements of a DNA chain also associated with adenosine triphosphate. Shulman's magnetic resonance studies have permitted the location of these heavy ions by ingenious triangulation methods. Also, he has found that the presence of these ions significantly reduces the yield of thymine radicals from irradiation.

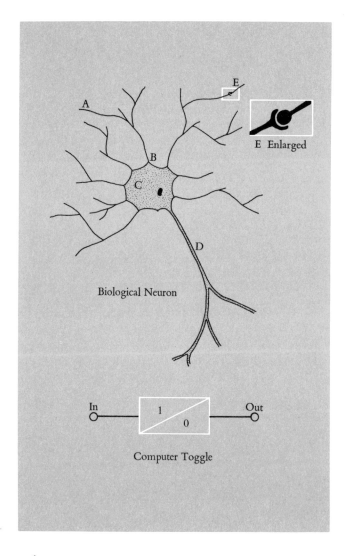

E Enlarged

Biological Neuron

In   1 / 0   Out

Computer Toggle

Fig. 16.
A highly schematic drawing of a biological neuron on the left shows various vital features indicated by letters. Among these, a junction E might be considered very crudely analogous to a computer toggle, which is diagramed on the right.

to generate electrical signals consistently and reproducibly enough so that a whole living pattern is controlled and even, in the case of higher organisms, rationalized by this communications net. We still know little of the molecular fine structure of neurons and perhaps even less about their mode of operation. But the great questions for the future of communications cannot avoid engaging us in an effort to probe into what neurons will tell us about the whole universe of natural and synthetic human communications systems.

Here we branch off into one of the newer techniques of research which originated in communications studies, that of systems research. (It will have a great impact on society in the future in other directions as well.) The example I shall give comes largely from Harmon's work with model neurons or neuromines, and is a rather dramatic departure from the specific studies of the basic elements of matter and of radiation that we have previously dealt with, for what we are trying with neuromines may have no structural relation to living neurons at all. They are what the systems analysts call black boxes, or what Professor John von Neumann called teleological research elements (Figure 16). They produce phenomena without the observer's knowing whether cause and effect can be precisely identified. It is turning out that these phenomena are telling us much about communication effects within organisms, especially man. Harmon constructs arrays of artificial neurons into which he can inject stimuli and from which he derives responses very similar to some of those found physiologically (Figure 17). In this way, slow but certain progress is being made toward finding some of the great sensitivities and economies of the communication of living things. As we have said before, once more the ability to replicate signals and to reproduce effects is a particularly striking quality of the living systems.

Harmon has recently been able to show with his neuron analogs the sorts of signals that seem to control such disciplined reproductions as the flight of insects. The zoologist D. M. Wilson, at the University of California, has studied the discharge patterns of the flight motor neurons of the desert locust (Figure 18). These have alternate double firings, and Harmon has been able to arrange two neuromines which were connected so that with a mutual inhibition these alternate double firings are readily produced. More than that, Harmon's experiments show an extraordinary range of properties even in so relatively simple a configuration of two units. Thus, with variation of the frequency of stimulus, he showed that the firing patterns change only in discrete steps (Figures 19 and 20). These studies are different indeed from investigations of the arbitrary coding of human speech by a telegraph key. But they show a deftness in the coding of information used in sophisticated forms by living mechanisms, systems far different than our most refined hardware in electronics and physical science. Our course toward true understanding of functions in these systems will be long and tortuous. We must be content with simulation of animation for some years to come.

However, there is an area in which this imitation of parts of organic information handling and communication is already

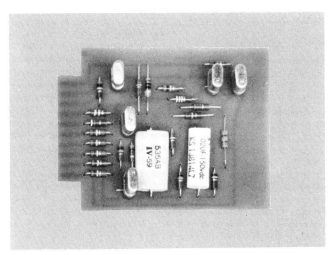

Fig. 17.
Here is shown a photograph of approxi-
mately natural size of Harmon's circuit
which replicates neuron electrical signaling.
For comparison is shown a hundredfold
magnification of a biological neuron, which
is doubtless far more versatile.

Electronic Neuron ×1

Biological Neuron ×100

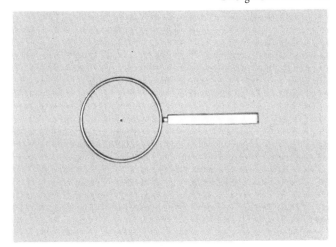

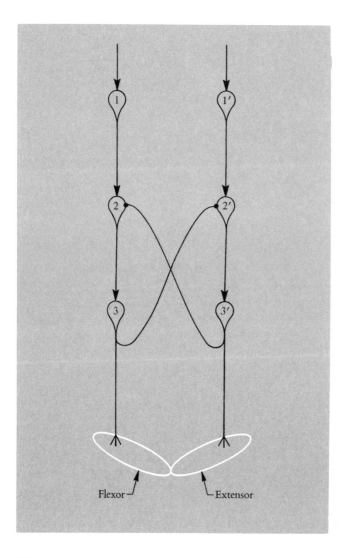

Flexor

Extensor

Fig. 18.
This schematic diagram suggests the possible neuron interconnections which control the flight system of an insect, the desert locust.

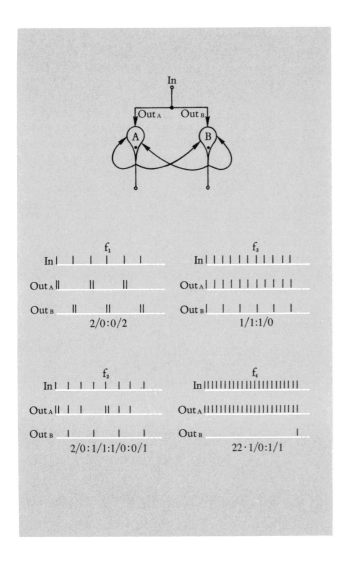

Fig. 19.

As before, a diagram at the top suggests methods of arrangement of neurons which are connected so that mutual inhibition and interaction can occur. Here, Harmon found that variation of stimulus frequency indicated at the top line of the various groupings of pulse patterns causes the indicated change of firing patterns in the output, in discrete steps. He also found that the pattern change caused by a given stimulus frequency depended on whether the frequency was approached from higher or lower values. Also, he noted that a deletion or injection of a single pulse in the stimulus pulse train was sufficient to control the natural selection of pulse patterns. The pulse patterns shown in the diagram are selected to reproduce or resemble patterns found by Wilson in the biological systems. In the diagram, the numbers at the bottoms of the groups of patterns are arranged so that each colon marks one stimulus period. Hence, $2/0:0/2$ means that for the first stimulus impulse, unit A fires twice, unit B not at all. For the second stimulus impulse A is silent while B fires twice. Then the whole pattern repeats. In the case for f_4, a multiplier is added since A fires 22 times while B is silent. Both A and B then fire once and the whole cycle repeats.

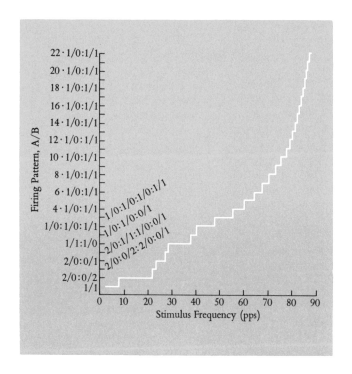

Fig. 20.
Here Harmon has found a whole series of firing patterns coming from an increase in stimulus frequency. Each pattern, as shown at the left of the graph, is stable over the indicated range of stimulus frequency and will repeat indefinitely under those conditions. At the extremes of the range the change is discontinuous.

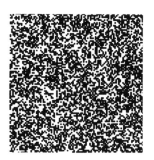 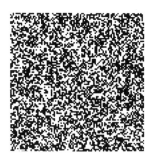

Fig. 21.
Random spot patterns have been generated by Julesz with a computer program which shifts patterns laterally by desired amounts so that precise depth effects are achieved without any cues from experience in the perception of known objects or situations. Some viewers may be able to superimpose the images by making the eyes accommodate to infinity.

changing our world. It is in the form of high-speed logic machines, where coupling of the representation of information in binary digit form as envisioned by information theory, with the prized human functions of abstract expression, such as in arithmetic, even algebra, calculus, and the representation of abstract forms, shapes, and sounds, has magnified some millionfold the reach of man to calculate in the past decade.

Let us look first at some cases where digital machines have provided methods for studying human information handling itself. Here one important psychological operation is visual perception. A central problem in such action is form recognition. This is classically conceived as some function of binocular depth perception. Julesz has found that by visual computer synthesis of truly random patterns, binocular depth perception or stereopsis can be studied effectively independently of the past experience in form recognition. Figure 21 shows a pair of such computer-generated patterns. If this figure were examined with ordinary stereoptic viewing devices, such as Polaroid spectacles when the illumination for each is polarized correspondingly, its three-dimensionality would be strongly perceived. Julesz's subsequent analysis of the various applications of these remarkably subjective facilities for studying the perception of organisms has revealed many remarkable and previously unknown qualities of this process. For example, Hering's early theory has been disproved and the necessary cues for stereopsis have been established.

In another astonishing advance in the use of machines, E. E. Zajac has created programs by which the high-speed computer manipulates an electron beam display device so that direct solutions of analytic problems are displayed. These can be photographed from the display as moving pictures (this is separate from the animation displays which form moving pictures directly according to the recently discovered techniques of K. C. Knowlton). A particularly beautiful example of the Zajac method is shown in the running displays of motions of a damped earth satellite shown in Figure 22 as a schematic rectangular box. All the proper motions of the satellite and the earth appear continuously and dynamically as the solutions to the appropriate equations are produced and directly depicted by the machine. Thus, the engineer has an astute extension of his senses. His design intuitions and associative sense of mechanical interactions can be easily and continuously coupled to a detailed display of the mathematical characteristics of the system he is studying. We have barely begun to see the revolutionary impact of this emerging capability on the whole domain of modern scientific experiment and engineering practice. By this technique may also be derived revolutionary educational schemes, since readily distributed computer programs can be called on to produce diagrams in geometry, in the physics of motion, and in mechanics, at all levels of sophistication.

Thus, the domain of pedagogic replication is also on the threshold of historic change in the sense that teaching is the transfer of concept whereby concepts can be reproduced in the minds of the learner. Since machines will be able to visualize explicitly abstractions which have been largely heretofore left to the inner mind of man, a new sense of manipulating the abstract is promised.

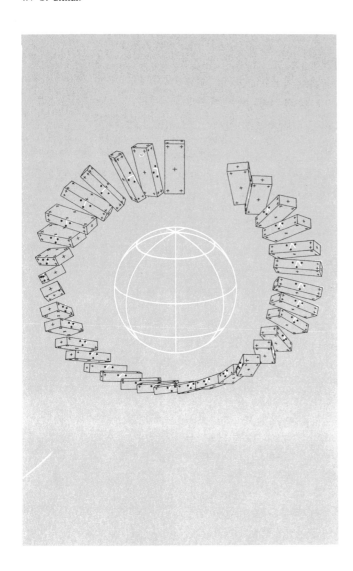

Fig. 22.
Composite drawing of a typical series of
scenes of a computer-produced orbit of
an earth satellite, being stabilized in
orientation, obtained by E. E. Zajac.
The box represents the earth satellite in
various positions determined by its typical
tumbling in an orbit. The effects of
damping out this tumbling can be
simultaneously displayed.